For Bess & Bartie
with affectionate regards
Bill

May. 14, 1948

Psychiatry: *Its Evolution and Present Status*

By WILLIAM C. MENNINGER, M.D.

Psychiatry

ITS EVOLUTION AND PRESENT STATUS

William C. Menninger, M.D.

CORNELL
UNIVERSITY PRESS

ITHACA, NEW YORK, 1948

❀❀❀❀❀❀❀❀❀❀❀❀❀❀❀❀❀❀❀❀❀❀

Preface

❀❀❀❀❀❀❀❀❀❀❀❀❀❀❀❀❀❀❀❀❀❀

THE MESSENGER LECTURES at Cornell University have long fulfilled the wish of their founder, Hiram Messenger, by sharing accumulated knowledge of "the evolution of civilization." The series of lectures in this volume discuss current concepts of man's mental processes which, in the area of medicine, have been designated psychiatry. During the nineteenth and early twentieth centuries medical science was more concerned with investigations of man's physiologic and chemical reactions than with explorations of his mental processes. Just why studies of man's real element of distinction from the lower animals escaped the attention of scientists is subject to speculation. Possibly because mental factors are intangible and difficult of measurement, scientists devoted their skills to biologic studies, where investigative procedures had been established. Deep-rooted superstitions and dogmas undoubtedly inhibited many investigators.

Whatever the reasons, progress in understanding man's anatomy, physiology, chemistry, and the pathologic changes caused by disease far surpassed the progress made in understanding the effects of his emotions. The old-time general practitioners, even though they lacked adequate scientific knowledge and instruments, were known for their skill in the art of medicine. They used effectively principles that modern psychiatry has organized and delineated. With the advent of modern medical education, general practitioners began to disappear from the American scene. Their places were taken by those representing the age of specialization in medicine. The latter physicians felt compelled to explain symptoms in terms of basic medical disciplines. They had little or no awareness of the patient's emotional reactions to love, fear, anger, and hate, which can be as real as diseased organs of the body and are capable of producing chronic disabilities, frequently as severe and usually more intolerable than organic diseases with recognized etiologic agents.

Fortunately the age of specialization in medicine produced a few individuals who were motivated by a desire to bring knowledge of man's mental processes to the level already achieved in the understanding of his physical functions. The era of modern psychiatry began with these few men. During the last quarter-century psychiatry has made as much progress as, if not more than, any other branch of medicine. Events in the world during this time contributed much. Our complex civilization with its many systems of belief unavoidably brings stress to persons whose beliefs differ from those who are in power. When power is exercised without regard for the consequences to the lives of other men, conflicts occur which may result in neuroses. These conflicts may be personal, familial, religious, economic, political, or racial.

In this volume Dr. William C. Menninger draws upon his vast experience and that of others in discussing the mechanisms involved in man's struggle with emotional conflicts. He portrays the background of psychiatry's growth and development in a brief history. He discusses the factors of resistance with which man is endowed to combat stress, and he tells what happens when resistance either collapses or is overwhelmed—a catastrophe not unlike that which occurs when bacteria overwhelm the body with infection. Dr. Menninger also calls attention to society's ills and suggests corrective measures based on observations and analyses of individuals.

If improvement in our individual, group, and community relations can stem from education, if the many symptoms and chronic ills of psychogenic etiology can be improved by educational clarification, then is it not the responsibility of great educational institutions to lead the way? The lectures which Dr. Menninger delivered at Cornell University and which are now published in this volume assist in meeting that challenge to higher education.

NORMAN MOORE, M.D.

The Messenger Lectures

In its original form this book consisted of three lectures delivered at Cornell University in the fall of 1947, namely, the Messenger Lectures on the Evolution of Civilization. That series was founded and its title prescribed by Hiram J. Messenger, B.Litt., Ph.D., of Hartford, Connecticut, who directed in his will that a portion of his estate be given to Cornell University and used to provide annually a "course or courses of lectures on the evolution of civilization, for the special purpose of raising the moral standard of our political, business, and social life." The lectureship was established in 1923.

Contents

Preface *Page v*

Chapter 1
Psychiatry: Its Evolution and Present Status
Page 1

Chapter 2
Psychoanalytic Psychiatry: Its Contribution
to the Understanding of Behavior
Page 49

Chapter 3
Psychiatry and the Social Order
Page 89

Index *Page 133*

Psychiatry: *Its Evolution and Present Status*

Chapter 1

Psychiatry:
Its Evolution and
Present Status

PSYCHIATRY, that branch of clinical medicine that concerns itself with the diagnosis, treatment, and prevention of personality disorders, probably enjoys a wider popular interest at the present time than does any other field of medicine. The apparently sudden increase in interest can be largely attributed to events connected with building an army and fighting a war.

There is no evidence that many persons, other than some psychiatrists, expected anything unusual to develop in this medical specialty as a result of the war. Even the War Department appears to have forgotten the psychiatric lessons of World War I. There was not even a vague indication that nearly two million selectees would be rejected as unacceptable for military service because of personality disorders, nor that over seven hundred thousand men [1] would be discharged from the service for the same reasons. Therefore when military leaders were faced with this major loss of man power and civilians became acquainted with the facts, investigations and speculations about the reasons were numerous.

The personal experience of the many individuals re-

---

[1] An extensive discussion of the statistics of both rejections and discharges for neuropsychiatric disorders and their significance was given by J. W. Appel, "Incidence of Neuropsychiatric Disorders in the United States Army in World War II," *Am. J. Psychiatry*, 102: 433–436 (Jan., 1946).

jected or discharged, plus the more or less direct contact of their families, friends, and employers with psychiatrists and psychiatry, answered some questions, but left many unanswered. News that great numbers of men and women did not qualify for military service piqued the public interest. Newspapers, magazines, radio, and screen, catering to this interest, have printed or presented an extensive series of articles, broadcasts, and plays related to psychiatry. They have capitalized upon our quite natural interest in ourselves.

Even though we regard ourselves as "normal," most of us confess to having "off days," blue periods, mood fluctuations, inefficient moments or days, occasional anti-social wishes. In the sense that these occur in all of us, they are "normal" reactions. Actually they indicate that something is wrong temporarily with our ability to adjust to the demands of the moment. Although we do not want to admit this fact, even to ourselves, we each have unexpressed fears and doubts that make themselves felt in occasional situations or under unusual circumstances. Most of us have some vague awareness of a relationship between our headaches and a stressful situation, or between our lack of appetite and persistent worry. We all have some difficulties with our elusive memories. We persist in maintaining strong prejudices. The psychiatrist considers these feelings as evidences of the psychopathology of everyday life and sees them as symptoms of the difficulty we have in solving problems. Under the stress of the war years, most of us became more conscious than ever before of the universality of psychological problems.

Spokesmen in every specialized field have difficulty in expressing themselves so that outsiders may understand. This has been particularly true for psychiatry. Even in these brief introductory remarks, I have used three terms that have specific meanings in psychiatry and thus require background information to be understood.

First, the word *personality* was used. This term is not synonymous with the mind, the soul, or any one particular aspect of the person. To the psychiatrist, the personality is the entire individual including mind, intelligence, emotions, organs, and all the rest of him. The personality embraces all his attributes—his physical structure and the way it functions, his loves and his hates, his play and his work, his reaction to his environment and to all those about him. The psychiatric use of "personality" covers all that a person has been, all that he is, and all that he is trying to become.

The word *normal* was used to indicate the concept of average behavior. A psychiatrist uses that term to refer to a wide range of behavior. He does not limit its use to the opposite of sickness or pathology. Our reactions, the outcome of our struggles, our work, our loves, and our hates, are determined by many factors—so many that no two of us behave identically. We differ not so much in the qualitative factors of our personalities as in the varying quantities or modifications of the characteristics that are common to all of us. For instance, every man has some love for himself, and most men have some love for other people or things; but it is the quantity of self-love that differentiates the "normal" from the "abnormal" personality. The wide variations make the concept of normality somewhat intangible and therefore of relatively minor significance as a measure of mental health.

The term *personality disorders* was used. The current interest in them is heightened by the realization that there may be a definite relationship between a headache and a distressing situation, between increased heart rate and fear, between continued work pressure and indigestion. Doctors, as well as laymen, are becoming more and more cognizant of the emotional factor in many illnesses.

A person functions as a unit. His total reaction involves organs, bones, muscles, nerves, emotions, and mind. Except for descriptive purposes his reaction cannot be separated into parts or segments. The older conception of a division into brain-mind-spirit versus body-soma-organism is no longer given credence. Every action and reaction, whether it is to bacteria or bullets, to teachers or parents, in loving or in hating, in health or in disease, is always a total response of the entire individual to the situation. That response will show varying mixtures of its three components: psychological, chemical, and physical. The acceptance of this relationship has been a long time coming.[2]

---

[2] This point of view in medicine, which recognizes the psychological and the physical reactions as interrelated, has been termed "psychosomatic," "psyche" referring to the psychological and "somatic" referring to the soma or the body. The majority of alert physicians have become aware of the term. A special medical or-

HISTORY OF THE EVOLUTION OF PSYCHIATRY

Psychiatry as a science is very young. In fact, many of us believe that the major portion of the useful and helpful information now composing its body of knowledge is the result of the contributions and stimulation of Freud, whose work began hardly sixty years ago.

The origin of many misconceptions about psychiatry and the many differing points of view of its practitioners lie much further back in the history of man's attempts to understand unusual thinking, and behavior, and actions. Earlier efforts set the stage for Freud and for our present-day concepts of dynamic interpretation of the personality. Only by reviewing some of these can we appreciate the tremendously powerful and persistent forces that have worked against the understanding of the personality and of mental illness.

It is debatable whether or not man's mistreatment of his mentally sick brothers is properly included in the history of the science of psychiatry. What the medicine men and witch hunters did can hardly be regarded as psychiatry, but knowledge of this is pertinent to a background review. Former attitudes toward mental illness and unusual behavior reflected current attitudes toward the worth of the individual personality, and therefore

---

ganization has developed for the study of psychosomatic problems, and a medical journal, *Psychosomatic Medicine*, is published monthly.

they should not be discussed in a spirit of condemnation. It is easy for us, from our present vantage point, to question how our forebears could have been so ignorant, stupid, fanatical, or cruel. We should keep in mind, however, that the historian of one hundred years hence will undoubtedly question how we, in this present day of enlightened appreciation of human worth, could permit such inadequate state care of mentally ill patients; how we could become so proficient in annihilating whole cities; how we could maintain irrational prejudices and tolerate a world so steeped with hate, suspicion, and war.

Medical historians disagree about whether the psychiatrist antedated the internist and the surgeon or followed them. The role of the physician came into being in response to sickness and suffering. Perhaps in the very early cultures folk practices took care of much of the illness. Apparently the magician, soothsayer, witch doctor, and medicine man built their reputations on the handling of those special cases that needed unusual help for the relief of suffering and pain. They were probably the first "experts" to devote full time and energy to the practice of healing.

Mental illness often was not identified as such among primitive people. Without a conspicuous physical disorder, pain, swelling, or disfigurement, there was no "cause" or focus to treat. Neither the patient himself nor the family considered him sick. As a matter of fact, this attitude toward the mentally afflicted is paralleled today. Curiously, it is sometimes the sickest personalities who refuse to admit that they are not well. When the family, through ignorance or fear, concurs, professional advice and treatment are not sought.

There are many instances in history, and even in some current cultures,[3] when the mentally sick person, recognized as being different from others, was regarded as being supernatural. He was thought to be infested by godly, animal, or devilish spirits. His strange and mysterious behavior was explained as being beyond his or anyone else's control unless supernatural help was called upon. If the infesting spirits were good, the victim was deified; and if evil, he was punished. The severely ill mental patient was placed, therefore, in the province of the priest, and thus insulated from medicine. Such a point of view was held by the public, by the medicine men or physicians, and probably also by the person so afflicted.

In great contrast to all who had preceded him, Hippocrates,[4] five centuries before Christ, was interested in personality problems as exhibited in mental illness, and had a considerable understanding of them. He wrote about them as a physician. Though many of his ideas were erroneous, some were in entire agreement with our present-day understanding; for instance, his ideas about delirium tremens and other forms of delirium. One of his major contributions was to deny the then current belief

[3] See chapter on "Incarnate Human Gods" in J. G. Frazer, *The Golden Bough* (New York: Macmillan Co., 1947), pp. 91–106.

[4] The psychiatric aspects of Hippocrates' work was well described by G. Zilboorg, *A History of Medical Psychology* (New York: W. W. Norton & Co., 1941), pp. 36–54.

in the sacred origin of disease and to attribute it to natural causes. This concept was lost sight of for a thousand years, but Hippocrates' influence continued, in part through the philosophers Plato and Aristotle, and prepared the way for the physicians Galen and Asclepiades.

Some degree of understanding of mental illness remained in evidence at least until the time of Caelius Aurelianus in the fifth century after Christ. Caelius, according to Iago Galdston, the medical historian, was not only a smart diagnostician but also a pre-eminent therapist of mental illness. His armamentarium of treatment techniques would do credit to any practicing psychiatrist today. It included psychotherapy, diet, exercise, massage, inunctions, baths, fresh air, heat, and medication as well as conversation and reading, theater performances, and traveling. He decried starving, restraints, and punishment.[5]

Then for a thousand years came the Dark Ages. By some historians this period is regarded as a gestation period for the Renaissance; without it the Renaissance could not have occurred. By others it has been referred to as the "epoch of retrogression." [6] Certainly during this time little or no progress was made in any field of science.

---

[5] I. Galdston, "Psychiatry and the History of Medicine," in *Modern Attitudes in Psychiatry: the March of Medicine, 1945* (New York: Columbia University Press, 1946), p. 12. See also S. E. Jelliffe, "Notes on the History of Psychiatry," *Alienist and Neurol.*, 33: 316–319 (1912).

[6] N. D. C. Lewis, *A Short History of Psychiatric Achievement* (New York: W. W. Norton & Co., 1941), p. 56.

In fact, some previous gains were lost. It was an age of devastating epidemics of cholera, the plague (known as the Black Death), leprosy, and scurvy. Religious movements were rampant and included such freakish performances as the Children's Crusades, in which young children marched thousands of miles. During holy wars and crusades to the Holy Land, thousands of men lost their lives attempting to find the holy grail. There were nation-wide epidemics of flagellation,[7] chorea, and tarantula dances,[8] all in the name of religious zeal.

During this time man's attitude toward mental illness was a mixture of mysticism and religiosity. The body was considered of no importance in comparison with the spirit and the soul. Judgment of behavior was grossly distorted in keeping with the misconceptions of the period. Man was thought to be the prey of demons, and his soul the battleground of the struggle between the devil and the Lord for its possession. An explanation of bizarre behavior was that the individual had become possessed by an animal or was a werewolf. Mystical figures and forces known as incubi and vampires, devils and witches were strongly believed to exist.

---

[7] See the *History of Flagellation,* which is described on the flyleaf as "a narrative of the strange customs and cruelties of the Romans, Greeks, Egyptians, etc. with an account of its practice among the early Christians as a religious stimulant and corrector of morals" (New York: Medical Publishing Co., 1903).

[8] H. Zinsser has given a short review of both chorea and tarantula dancing in the tenth to thirteenth centuries, (*Rats, Lice and History* [Boston: Atlantic Monthly Press–Little, Brown, & Co., 1935], pp. 80–84).

In 1486 the *Malleus Maleficarum* ("The Witches' Hammer"), written by two Dominican friars, was published. This book was for the use of the full-time inquisitors stationed in every city. It described in detail the behavior, symptoms, method of conviction, and punishment of witches.[9]

That same year probably marked the birth of Cornelius Agrippa (1486?–1535), who was one of the first physicians to revolt against the inhuman beliefs of the day. He scathingly criticized his professional contemporaries and their practice of medicine. He is important in the background of psychiatry because, during the last three years of his life, he took to live with him a young medical student, Johann Weyer (1515–1588). By his determination Weyer, as much as any other man, was responsible for the eventual inclusion of the treatment of behavior disorders (now psychiatry) in the practice of medicine. It is significant that his books were banned, chiefly because they denied the existence of witches.

The year after Columbus discovered America, 1493, was the probable birth year of another physician who is famous in the history of psychiatry, a man known to us as Paracelsus.[10] He was a courageous, tempestuous, turbulent soul who conceived of man as a miniature of the cosmos, inseparably related to it. This concept was the

[9] Zilboorg, who has written a most complete history of psychiatry, gave a specially full description of the *Malleus Maleficarum* in *A History of Medical Psychology*.

[10] His original name was Theophrastus Bombastus von Hohenheim.

basis of Paracelsus' extensive attempt to interpret man in relation to the world. He forecast our currently accepted view of man as a biological and social entity, directly related to the world in which he lives.

From this period on, scientific discoveries were numerous. During the sixteenth and seventeenth centuries, in all the sciences knowledge grew rapidly. There were the spectacular discoveries of Galileo (1564–1642) with regard to the telescope and the laws of motion. His contemporary, Kepler (1571–1630), discovered the planetary system. Both men were persecuted and imprisoned. In order to find places in which they might be allowed to work, they traveled over much of Europe. Newton (1642–1727) established the laws of gravitation, which are the basis of our theories of mechanics.

This great scientific progress was shared by medicine. Two years after the death of Paracelsus in 1541, Andreas Vesalius published his *De Humani Corporis Fabrica*, which was particularly concerned with the brain and the nervous system. In comparatively rapid succession came the discovery of the microscope, attributed to Zacharias Janssen, 1590, and of the circulation of the blood by William Harvey (1578–1657); the first identification of microorganisms by Anton van Leeuwenhoek (1632–1723); and the formulation of a sound basis for an understanding of physiology by Albrecht von Haller (1708–1777).

While remarkable discoveries in science and in medicine were in the making, those few physicians who worked with the "insane" attempted to formulate their concepts of mental illness. This necessitated a divorce of these afflicted persons from the taint of sin and shame that religion had given them. Because of the physical nature of the medical discoveries, the early concepts of mental illness were developed from the mechanistic point of view that then permeated all medicine. The new and gratifying knowledge—of anatomy and physiology, of the physical origin of various diseases, of measures of physical treatment—became the chief bases of orientation and approach to most medical problems. This "organic" approach applied to psychiatry. The more intangible factors of feeling, thinking, emotion, and behavior were largely ignored.

Through this era, mentally afflicted people—we cannot call them patients—who received attention were segregrated from the community and given over to the care of attendants, who played the role of prison keepers while they provided their charges with the poorest of food, straw beds, and vermin-infested quarters. Those unfortunates were usually kept in chains in unlighted, unsanitary cells and were rarely given any medical treatment. In some instances purging, bloodletting, and starvation were considered therapy.

It was not until 1792, hardly 150 years ago, that a courageous French physician first took those individuals out of their chains, dungeons, and unsanitary rooms, and treated them as patients. This Frenchman, Philippe Pinel (1745–1826), brought about this reform against the greatest of opposition when he initiated the so-called "open-door" policy in the treatment of hospitalized psychiatric patients.

Through the next one hundred years, the evolution of psychiatry was greatly speeded by the enlightenment resulting from the work of Pinel and the English layman, William Tuke, who carried out a similar reform movement in England in the name of the Friends Society. A Massachusetts school teacher, Dorothea Lynde Dix,[11] crusaded in America so effectively that asylums were built for mentally ill patients.

Much of the advance in formulating theories of psychiatric illness was made in terms of the prevalent mechanistic point of view. Mental illness was regarded as being due chiefly to organic causes. Laborious efforts were spent in building classifications and detailed descriptions of each disease entity. Treatment consisted largely of mechanical procedures—bleeding, purging, whirling, ducking, and so forth.

Hospitalized patients were the sole source of new clinical knowledge for later psychiatric study. Minute symptom description and rather rigid classification of patients' behavior by superficial and largely external appearances provided a worth-while base line. This kind

[11] A. Deutsch, *The Mentally Ill in America* (Garden City, N.Y.: Doubleday, Doran & Co., 1937), pp. 158–185; also H. E. Marshall, *Dorothea Dix, Forgotten Samaritan* (Chapel Hill: University of North Carolina Press, 1937).

of psychiatry is comparable to the daguerreotype era of photography. The diagnostic picture was a crude representation of the sick personality, showing many defects in the method of study and technique. Nevertheless it was important progress.

A most important forward step in the history of psychiatry occurred when Franz Anton Mesmer (1734–1815) acted upon an idea expressed by Paracelsus many years before:

One should with diligence, take note of the spirit of man, of which there are really two, that are inborn.

For this is indeed true, that man is in the image of God and thereby has a Godly Spirit in him; but, on the other hand, man is also an animal, and as such has an animal spirit. These spirits are two antagonists, and yet the one must soften the other.[12]

It is the opinion of Galdston that Mesmer, who is frequently portrayed as a fakir and a charlatan, was merely a stupid man who bumped into the phenomenon of suggestion and suggestibility, which was far too complex for his comprehension. But he not only saw the importance of the psychic power of suggestion but also its use in psychological therapy.

It was Mesmerism, or animal magnetism, that John Elliotson (1791–1868) tried out as an anesthetic in sur-

---

[12] Quoted from Galdston, *op. cit.*, p. 22, quoting from Paracelsus' book *Die Lunatici*.

gery, and that later was given the name of hypnotism [13] by an English surgeon, James Braid. Charcot, the famous neurologist in the Salpêtrière Hospital in Paris, became acquainted with hypnosis. Although he did not understand it, he used it widely and apparently helpfully. Two Frenchmen, Liébeault and Bernheim of Nancy used hypnotism extensively as a treatment measure and showed it to be a form of suggestion. Sigmund Freud, in 1885, went to Paris to study hypnosis with Charcot and, four years later, with Liébeault and Bernheim.

Thus through Paracelsus to Mesmer to Braid to Charcot to Liébeault and Bernheim, we finally come to Freud (1856–1939). Freud, a neurologist, became interested in the most commonly recurring clinical problem—the neurosis—at about the age of thirty-five. He devoted the remainder of his life to developing that most productive of all psychiatric contributions—psychoanalysis. Oberndorf [14] has divided Freud's work into three general periods: the period of theory development, 1890 to 1905; the period of clinical application, 1905 to 1920; and the period of philosophical reflection, 1920 to 1938. It is to Freud that we owe much of psychiatry as we now know and practice it. His formulations of the structure

---

[13] The historical development of hypnotism is well described by M. Brenman, and M. M. Gill, *Hypnotherapy: A Survey of the Literature* (New York: International Universities Press, 1947), pp. 3–14.

[14] C. P. Oberndorf, "Sigmund Freud: His Work and Influence," *Am. J. Psychiatry*, 93: 21–28 (July, 1936). See also F. Alexander, "Sigmund Freud (1856–1939)," *Psychosomatic Med.*, 2: 68–73 (Jan., 1940).

of the personality, infantile development, methods of investigating and treating personality disorders, the unconscious, and many other observations have given us the solid base for what is termed *dynamic psychiatry*.

Throughout this historical chain from Paracelsus to Freud, psychiatry was characterized by its primary interest in understanding behavior and psychological treatment. The outstanding feature of psychiatry today is not its classification or description of disease entities but its knowledge of the dynamic forces operative in the personality.

In a historical review of its evolution, one cannot ignore the effects, at least on American psychiatry, of World Wars I and II. Dr. Thomas Salmon is credited with having described World War I as playing Prince Charming to the medical Cinderella, psychiatry. Galdston has suggested that, as a result of World War II, psychiatry has become, at least in the eyes of some portion of the public, a pin-up girl.

The two wars gave a tremendous impetus to a more intelligent acceptance and utilization of psychiatry by the medical profession. In the military services psychiatrists worked with specialists in the other branches of medicine. By utilizing the standard procedure of working closely in conjunction with clinical psychologists and psychiatric social workers, psychiatrists gave a better quality of psychiatric treatment to patients. As far as can be judged from the records, little difference appeared in the conclusions about the role psychiatry played in

World War II as compared with World War I.[15] However, the scientific progress of the intervening years, 1918 to 1941, plus the much greater number of people involved and the much longer duration of World War II, headlined the conclusions in much larger letters.

Particularly in World War II were psychiatrists able to serve in new ways. Their services were called for and demanded far beyond the confines of the hospital ward. From the beginning of the war they participated in the process of the selection of men in the draft; later on they helped select the men who were sent overseas and "screened" those who were to be redeployed to another theater of action. They were asked to evaluate the training methods in terms of their effect on mental health and morale in camps and on posts. They were expected to recommend measures to prevent mental ill health. They advised the establishment of a "tour of duty" for the infantry soldier,[16] i.e., a definite length of time that a man would have to stay continuously in combat. They emphasized the importance of the motivation of soldiers toward wanting to fight, and many other points. In addition to being a medical science, military psychiatry had

[15] T. W. Salmon, "War Neuroses and Their Lesson," *N.Y. Med. J.*, 109: 993–994 (June 7, 1919); also W. C. Menninger, "Psychiatric Experience in the War, 1941–1946," *Am. J. Psychiatry*, 103: 577–586 (March, 1947).

[16] One of the famous official psychiatric documents of the war considered specially the problem of the tour of duty for the infantry soldier. This was written by J. W. Appel and G. W. Beebe. It was reprinted under the title of "Preventive Psychiatry," *J.A.M.A.*, 131: 1469–1475 (Aug. 31, 1946).

to become in some degree a social science [17] because of
its concern with environmental factors in illness.

THE STATUS OF PSYCHIATRY TODAY

From this brief historical sketch, one may see and
understand more clearly that certain features of the
current practice of psychiatry can be directly traced
to events in the distant past. The many misconceptions [18]
with which psychiatry is still cursed stem from the beliefs
of the dark ages: that the soul and the body are separate,
that misbehavior and sin are synonymous, that irrational
behavior is mysterious, unexplainable, and shameful.

We can see many conspicuous traces of the mechanistic era when, for very good reasons, medicine was
purely materialistic. The residual influence in our medical school curricula is all too evident in the dispro-
portionate emphasis still placed upon the study of physical anatomy, physical causes of disease, mechanical
measures for diagnosis, and physical and chemical treatment measures. The assumption is still prevalent that,
except for extreme cases, disorders of feeling, thinking,
and acting are not medical problems. A few psychiatrists
permit themselves to be completely preoccupied with

[17] F. J. Braceland, "Psychiatric Lessons from World War II,"
Am. J. Psychiatry, 103: 587–593 (March, 1947); W. C. Menninger,
"Lessons from Military Psychiatry for Civilian Psychiatry," *Mental
Hyg.*, 30: 571–589 (Oct., 1946).

[18] There are many other misconceptions that are well outlined
and discussed by M. Levine, *Psychotherapy in Medical Practice*
(New York: Macmillan Company, 1942), pp. 3–16.

the description and classification of the very severe mental illnesses. They continue to search for organic causes of all types of mental disease. The number who so limit their efforts is rapidly diminishing. There are, however, some psychiatrists in America, and probably many more in certain foreign countries, who still consider all behavior in terms of heredity, anatomy, chemistry, or physiology. To be sure, we must learn far more than we now know about the anatomy, the chemistry, and the physiology of the brain and the nervous system. Such additional knowledge would contribute greatly to our better understanding of behavior. But that is not enough.

The most conspicuous aspect of psychiatric practice today is its major interest in the effect of experience and environment on the way people feel, think, and behave. Most psychiatrists concern themselves with the dynamics of why a person becomes what he is and why he does what he does, and whether his behavior is "normal" or pathological.

The most recent important influence on psychiatry has been the varied experiences in the handling of great masses of people. These have forced psychiatric consideration of the social influences in everyday life that mark the path toward or away from the sickbed. About the time of World War I, psychiatry was first applied to human relations in industry. Military practice indicated its potential value for the prevention of civilian mental ill health.

Increasingly after World War I the help of psychiatrists was utilized in criminal and juvenile courts and in penal institutions. Following the war there was beginning recognition that it was important for school teachers to have knowledge of the emotional development of children. Mental health counseling services were first established in colleges and universities about 1919. All of these applications of psychiatric information and service have resulted in increasing interest in the area now identified as social psychiatry. Since World War II it has received special attention from many more psychiatrists, laymen, organizations, and institutions.

As a result of these recent experiences, psychiatry is in the midst of a period of transition and redirection. It is still in an eruptive state, expanding rapidly, increasing its perspectives and its contacts. One example of this is that only sixty per cent of its practitioners are now located in state hospitals, a decrease of twenty per cent in the last twenty years. In other words, more psychiatrists are concerned with a broader field of practice in the office, general hospital, outpatient clinic, and various social organizations. In increasing numbers they are concerning themselves more and more with the minor (less severe) types of personality disorders, the neuroses, and recognizing the emotional component in all illness. The handwriting is clear that in the near future there will be much more emphasis on the formulation and widespread adoption of measures that will aid in the maintenance of good mental health.

INTERRELATIONSHIPS

The present-day discipline of psychiatry, built as it is around the dynamics of the personality, finds itself, perforce, concerned with the social relationships of that personality because of the organization of our culture. Therefore its field of influence impinges upon and in some cases overlaps the fields of various social sciences, as well as those of law, religion, and education. As yet, many of these relationships are not too clear or definite. Neither psychiatry nor the other disciplines are firmly united in defining the areas where co-operative effort is desirable. Therefore any discussion of this subject can only represent one person's point of view and opinion.

So far, psychiatry as a branch of medical science has developed an intimate, close-working relationship with two social sciences, namely, psychology and social work. With two others—anthropology and sociology—it shares many common interests and, as a consequence, the scientific contributions of each are of value to the other. Psychiatrists have made a few formal and many informal contacts with religious leaders.

PSYCHIATRY AND MEDICINE

Psychiatry became a part of medicine because of its inclusion by physicians and not because of popular recognition or public demand. It remains a *speciality of medicine* because of the fact that disturbances of the emotions and organ functions cannot be separated into "physical" and "mental" illness. A headache may be a symptom of measles, of worry, of indigestion, of brain tumor, or of many other clinical entities. Physical disorders may give rise to mental symptoms, and psychological conflicts may lead to serious deviations from the normal in the functioning of the various organs of the body.

In many ways, however, psychiatry still stands apart from medicine in the popular mind. The average person has a reasonably clear concept of physical ill health. He can recognize it in himself and in others. While he may consider the behavior of other people as queer or bizarre or confused, he is not likely to relate it to their health. Nor does he consider mental distress in himself to be a medical problem. As a matter of fact, some physicians who are not oriented psychiatrically re-enforce this attitude when they get rid of the patient with nonorganic symptoms by saying, "It's all in your mind," "Get away from it all," or "Take a little vacation."

Psychiatry does differ from other medical specialties in that, instead of treating painful symptoms of tangible and visible damage to an organ, it deals with equally painful but relatively intangible symptoms of disturbed feelings, perceptions, intellection, and behavior. Psychiatric problems must be approached differently from those of physical ill health. Because of their complicated nature, personality problems require far more time for study and evaluation than do those of almost any other type of illness. Psychiatric medicine must take into consideration the role of environmental and social situations in causing the illness of its patients, whereas in no other branch of medicine is this routinely essential.

Unhappily, too often psychiatry still stands apart from medicine in the physician's mind. The fundamental facts of medical education are based upon knowledge gained from physics and chemistry and biology. In medical school the student starts his study with anatomy, physiology, and biochemistry. During his four years he becomes well oriented to the hows, whys, and wherefores of the physical aspects of body function. He learns to prescribe drugs and medicines and to perform various types of surgery. He graduates into his profession as a Doctor of Medicine thinking of the human being in anatomical and chemical terms, almost completely ignorant of the psychological factors that operate in the personality in illness or in health.[19]

The psychiatrist-to-be must acquire special additional knowledge that the general medical and surgical physician has little opportunity to learn. He needs to know about the anatomy and physiology of the personality and how these are affected by various environmental factors such as the experiences and training in childhood, the stress and strain of external and internal conflicts, and so

---

[19] Recently a very extensive study of the place of psychiatry in medical education has been reported by the Group for the Advancement of Psychiatry in a special printed report on *Medical Education*, March, 1948. This analyzes in considerable detail the subject matter and methods of teaching of undergraduate psychiatry as well as graduate training in psychiatry.

forth. Not until relatively recently have the dynamics of the personality and the principles of psychiatric treatment been formulated sufficiently clearly and simply to be presented to the medical student. As a consequence the teaching of dynamic psychiatry in medical schools has been nil or minimal. Even today all the psychiatry taught constitutes, at most, not more than 4 or 5 per cent of the total number of hours in the curriculum. Unfortunately, in most medical schools the subject is given not more than 2 per cent of the teaching hours. This lack would be less serious if the basic principles of dynamic psychiatry permeated the teaching about other medical specialties.

There is however, a very definite light of hope on the horizon of medical education. Several medical schools have recently increased the number of hours devoted to the teaching of this subject.[20] Some professors in other branches of medicine are beginning to teach their students how to identify the emotional components in illness and what to do about them.

Through many media graduate physicians are becoming more and more aware of the emotional factors that cause or aggravate or prevent illness, both physical and mental. In the Army and the Navy doctors of all medical

---

[20] The passage of Public Law 487 at the Seventy-ninth Congress, an amendment to the Public Health Service Act known as the National Mental Health Act, has provided funds for research, community demonstrations, and psychiatric education. Through funds from this source several medical schools have been given the finances to develop or expand their departments of psychiatry.

specialties found themselves working harmoniously side by side. Psychiatric consultations were frequent in medical and surgical wards. Psychiatry is an integral part of the hospital services in the Veterans Administration. In several university hospitals psychiatry is practiced and taught, not in a psychiatric pavilion as such, but in general medical wards. Psychiatrists practicing in the community serve as interpreters of psychological medicine to other physicians. A leading internist who is the dean of a medical school recently stated:

The practitioner in all fields of medicine is confronted today with a major challenge, which is the recognition and proper handling of patients with functional disease. It is a challenge that he can and must meet, but in order to do so he must equip himself with additional knowledge of some of the precepts and techniques of psychiatric practice.[21]

Indeed, one can feel justified optimism about the progress in increasing the acceptance by physicians of the helpful body of knowledge gained from psychiatry.

PSYCHIATRY AND PSYCHOLOGY

Psychology is a science that is as yet poorly integrated. It encompasses the description, exploration, and theoretical explanation of all behavior phenomena. Originally this was done in terms of brain, spinal cord, and nerve function. As generally taught and practiced, psychology

---

[21] J. T. Wearn, "The Challenge of Functional Disease," *J.A.M.A.*, 134: 1517–1520 (Aug. 30, 1947).

is a presentation of the "laws" of behavior and learning
and the testing of various abilities and tendencies.

Clinical psychology is a specialized subdivision of the
general field. The adjective "clinical" refers specifically
to and implies an active interest in the treatment of illness
or maladjustment. Preparation of the clinical psychologist should involve an integrated presentation of the
psychology of learning, comparative psychology, developmental psychology, psychoanalytic theory, social psychology, and psychology of the normal and of the
abnormal. As yet the field is in the process of definition,
and such comprehensive practice does not exist.[22]

The clinical psychologist works directly in association
with physicians and assists them in the diagnosis and
treatment of mental maladjustment. In our best psychiatric centers the clinical psychologist is a member of
a close-working staff team. He administers and in-
terprets a battery of psychological tests that provide information about the patient that neither the patient nor
his associates could give the doctor during an exhaustive
mental examination and social history. The data so obtained have become as important to the understanding of
the patient as are the urinalysis,[23] the blood tests, and the
physical examination. "The diagnostic function of the

---

[22] Several of the points made in this presentation of clinical psychology were suggested to me by Dr. David Rapaport, the director
of the Department of Research of the Menninger Foundation and
an outstanding clinical psychologist.

[23] K. A. Menninger, "Clinical Psychology in the Psychiatric
Clinic," *Bull. Menninger Clin.*, 7: 89–92 (May, 1943).

clinical psychologist is now so well established in psychiatry that the competent psychiatrist . . . would no more exclude the special techniques of the psychologist in his diagnostic studies than would a capable internist routinely exclude the findings of the roentgenologist." [24]

Molly Harrower [25] has stated her hope "for the clinical psychologist to emerge in a more positive role" of what might be called "the assessor, surveyor or map maker of the individual's potentialities and resources. Thus his task would not lie in the diagnosis of a neurosis, but rather in a description of the type of personality in which neurotic symptoms were finding expression."

At the present moment, one of the specially moot questions about the relationship between clinical psychology and psychiatry is concerned with whether the psychologist is qualified to treat patients. Physicians appreciate that any relationship of the doctor or of any of his staff to the patient is interpreted by the patient as a part of the treatment. Therefore the psychological examination is, in some instances, definitely a therapeutic, as well as an examinational, procedure. There are some clinical psychologists who have sufficient experience and training to give effective psychological treatment. But

[24] K. A. Menninger, "Psychiatry and Psychology," *Bull. Menninger Clin.*, 11: 45–49 (March, 1947); also in *American Psychologist*, 2: 139–140 (April, 1947).

[25] M. R. Harrower, "The Evolution of a Clinical Psychologist," in *Training in Clinical Psychology* (New York: Josiah Macy, Jr., Foundation, 1947), p. 13.

there are many who are doing treatment whose only training has been "picked up" as they went along.[26] Their training has recently been the subject of intensive consideration and recommendations.[27]

Every clinical psychologist must have a sound understanding of treatment if he is to work with physicians, and this means he must have some training in this field. This training experience, however, is not implied, even by the clinical psychologists themselves, as having the intent of turning the group into therapists. On this point a committee of training for clinical psychology reported, "It is our hope that, despite the very great social need for the increase of available therapists, few psychologists will be drawn into this work [treatment] to the extent that it is their sole occupation. We believe that the major contribution of the psychologist lies rather in research." [28]

Physicians feel very strongly that to them belongs the sole responsibility for treating illness, physical or mental. They have spent long years in study and under

---

[26] M. Brenman, in *Training in Clinical Psychology*, p. 71.

[27] *The Place of Psychology in an Ideal University*, The Report of the University Commission to Advise on the Future of Psychology at Harvard, Alan Gregg, Chairman (Cambridge: Harvard University Press, 1947). The relationship of psychology to psychiatry is touched upon (p. 34).

[28] "Report of the Committee on Training in Clinical Psychology of the American Psychological Association," Detroit, Sept. 9–13, 1947, Chairman, Dr. David Shakow, *Am. Psychologist*, 2: 539–558 (Dec., 1947).

supervision as a protection against wrong practices. Consequently, unless the clinical psychologist works in a medical group and is trained in therapeutic methods, treatment should not be a part of his job. On a medical staff some clinical psychologists equipped by training can render valuable aid in treatment. But the physician must assume full responsibility for that treatment, just as he does with other nonmedical therapists.

Unfortunately there are some psychologists who have separated themselves from medical associates, changed their title from clinical to consulting psychologist, and have pretended to practice psychiatric medicine. Such procedure is lamented by both psychiatrists and clinical psychologists. Moreover, every available and qualified person is needed for psychological testing and therapy in the various medical organizations in the country.[29]

Some specially trained psychologists are excellently qualified as counselors (but not as clinical workers) to advise about the very real problems of vocational choice and adjustment, remedial reading, speech training, and premarital and marital counseling where mental ill health is not involved. Counseling that deals with gross mental maladjustment is primarily a medical responsibility. Fortunately the great majority of the leading clinical psychologists are associated intimately with medical groups.

---

[29] D. Blain, "The Psychiatrist and the Psychologist," *J. Clin. Psychol.*, 3: 4–10 (Jan., 1947).

PSYCHIATRY AND SOCIAL WORK

Social work and its specific offshoot, *psychiatric social work*, is the second essential discipline in the psychiatric team. Medical social work has been an active field for many years, but psychiatric social work as a specialty began at the Boston Psychopathic Hospital in 1913 under Dr. Elmer Ernest Southard and Miss Mary C. Jarrett.[30] It was furthered by the inauguration of a special training course in psychiatric social work at Smith College in 1918. Now many other schools offer such specialized training.

Social case work, that is, the meeting of the social needs of an individual, has long dealt with a wide range of social and personal problems. Many of these are purely materialistic in nature—finances, housing, employment, medical care, and similar problems. Psychiatric social case work developed through a recognition of the fact that in many, if not all, such instances one needed to know how the person felt and thought, and the relation of these feelings and thoughts to his practical problems. This required that those social workers who were particularly interested in that aspect of their work obtain additional training in psychiatry. These became the psychiatric social workers.[31]

More than any other branch of medicine, psychiatry

[30] K. A. Menninger, *The Human Mind* (3d ed., New York: Alfred A. Knopf, 1945), p. 420.

[31] G. D. Bibring, "Psychiatry and Social Work," *J. Soc. Work.*, 28: 203–211 (June, 1947).

needs to know about and understand the environment in which the patient lives. Too often the only source of such information is the patient himself, or his relatives when they are available. Therefore, one of the first contributions that psychiatric social work makes to psychiatry is the direct contact by the social worker with various persons with whom the patient lives or works. From these persons the social worker can piece together a fairly objective picture of the environment, which is of immense value to the psychiatrist.

Not only is the psychiatric social worker of direct aid in reporting his findings of the environmental situation, but also he is taught how to organize this information into what is known as the "social history." His training in psychiatry provides him with the background to understand personality development, psychopathology, psychological factors in the family, and interpersonal relationships. These points are the object of special scrutiny in his examination of that environment. He is thus equipped to bring the psychiatrist many psychological data that would be missed by the social case worker without psychiatric training.

The psychiatric social worker also serves as the tool to implement the psychiatrist's suggestions as to desirable changes in that environment. He has the responsibility of orienting key people, advising relatives, and bringing about changes in personal relationships as well as in the physical situation.[32]

[32] E. L. Ginsburg, "The Training and Function of a Psychiatric

The psychiatric social worker has the dual responsibility of evaluating problems that originate not only in the external situation but also within the person himself. In recommending remedial measures he must of necessity be aware of the results of those changes; he must know how to relieve tensions and how to give new confidence. By the very nature of his work, therefore, he becomes a counselor, an advisor, and a therapist.

"All psychiatric social work is undertaken in direct and responsible working relationship with psychiatry." [33] While his actual practice in the hospital differs somewhat from that in the clinic, in all cases the social worker becomes not only an investigator but invariably a therapist. His therapy is primarily directed toward helping the individual accept the situation, modifying the external factors insofar as this is possible. It differs from the psychiatrist's treatment in that the social worker rarely attempts to change the structure of the personality; rather does he help the individual to live with his personality. [34] Case work treatment, therefore, depends both on knowledge of the environment and of the individual.

Psychiatric social work brings another major contribution to psychiatry, because of the direct contact

Social Worker in the Clinical Setting," in *Training in Clinical Psychology*, pp. 51–52.

[33] *The Psychiatric Social Worker in the Psychiatric Hospital*, report No. 2 of the Group for the Advancement of Psychiatry, compiled by the Committee on Psychiatric Social Work, Jan., 1948.

[34] Elizabeth Ross, "The Training and Function of a Psychiatric Social Worker in the Clinical Setting," in *Training in Clinical Psychology*, p. 52.

with the environment by the worker. It is a rare occasion when the psychiatrist sees the environment first hand, and, therefore, social workers through their personal knowledge become realists in evaluating its stresses and support. For these many reasons psychiatric social work has become the indispensable handmaiden to psychiatry.

PSYCHIATRY AND ANTHROPOLOGY

Originally anthropology limited itself to inquiries regarding man's origin. Gradually its scope increased to include comparisons of differences in anatomy, psychology, geographical location, language, and culture of racial and social groups of people. According to Kluckhohn,[35] prior to 1920 anthropology focused its attention upon the standard, or average, cultural pattern. Then came the realization that culture was manifested in a concrete way only by the individual and, hence, that it was valuable to obtain personal documents. When the individual was recognized as a legitimate object of anthropological study, the way was opened for collaboration with psychiatry.

The training of the average psychiatrist has not provided him with information about the social sciences.

---

[35] C. Kluckhohn, "The Influence of Psychiatry on Anthropology," in *One Hundred Years of American Psychiatry (1844-1944)*, ed. by G. Zilboorg and J. K. Hall (New York: Columbia University Press, 1944), pp. 589-615.

For this reason few psychiatrists are familiar with the contributions that anthropology has made and can make to the understanding of the individual. Only rarely do presentations of an anthropological nature appear in psychiatric literature, at least that which routinely comes to the attention of most of the psychiatrists. There are only a few anthropologists such as Benedict, Roheim, Devereux, and Mead [36] whose writings, because of the authors' firsthand acquaintance with psychiatry and psychoanalysis, have been of particular interest to psychiatrists. Yet both disciplines believe that the personality and culture are derived from the interplay between human needs and the external world.[37]

Psychiatrists have been accustomed to identify the regression to infantile (uninhibited) behavior that occurs in some types of severe mental illness as "primitive." This is because they consider the instinctive and undisguised expressions of desire as "primitive," i.e., unmodified by learned control. Without recognizing a difference in the semantics of the two disciplines, psychiatrists have been prone to equate primitive behavior with social practices

---

[36] According to Kluckhohn, Edward Sapir was the first great influence among anthropologists toward the application of psychiatric knowledge to anthropology. Both Benedict and Mead wrote on subjects of special interest to psychiatrists. Roheim was trained as an analyst. Devereux is associated with a psychiatric hospital.

[37] H. L. Witmer, "Some Parallels Between Dynamic Psychiatry and Cultural Anthropology," *Am. J. Orthopsychiat.*, 9: 95–101 (Jan., 1939).

35

in anthropologically described primitive societies. This has been a comparison of incomparables.[38]

With the intertranslation of terminologies, anthropology can contribute to psychiatry specifically in two ways:

(1) "The psychiatrist could wish for no better substantiations of the content of the unconscious among members of our society than to find at least some of its phases consciously recognized and institutionalized, that is unrepressed, in other societies.[39]

(2) "The careful study of primitive societies is important today . . . because they provide case material for the study of cultural forms and processes. They help us to differentiate between those responses that are specific to local cultural types and those that are general to mankind. Beyond this, they help us to gauge and understand the immensely important rôle of culturally conditioned behavior."[40]

Psychiatry, particularly through the psychoanalytic approach, has contributed to anthropology, perhaps most importantly in the discovery that the individual's life, and therefore his thinking, feeling, and acting, is shaped by the social setting in which he spends his childhood. Psychiatry has provided a basis for the study of the adjustment of the individual to social demands and social

[38] C. Dubois, "Some Anthropological Perspectives on Psychoanalysis," *Psychoanal. Rev.*, 24: 246–263 (July, 1937).
[39] *Ibid.*
[40] Ruth Benedict, *Patterns of Culture* (Boston and New York: Houghton Mifflin Co., 1934), p. 20.

forms. The identification of cultural themes and patterns has been attempted in psychiatric terms by Ruth Benedict.[41] Psychiatric knowledge has also proved useful in surveying cultural influences on the personality and the character formation of various ethnic groups. Undoubtedly anthropological studies have gained a deeper insight into cultures through the psychoanalytic interpretation of customs, folklore, and dreams. Deviations from tribal ideals can also be interpreted in terms of psychodynamic principles.

As psychiatric understanding has increased among anthropologists, it has led them to recognize the incompleteness of the question-and-answer method of investigation. It has emphasized the need for passive interviews, for controlled observations, for simple experiments, for personal documents, dreams, fantasies of individuals, and other informal material.[42]

There are numerous evidences of an increasingly close working relationship between psychiatrists and anthropologists. Many workers in both fields recognize not only the importance of the contributions they can make to each other, but the importance of combining their efforts for better results in both fields. To date, anthropologists have probably made much more use of the findings from dynamic psychiatry than have the psychiatrists of anthropological data.

---

[41] *Ibid.*, p. 20.
[42] Kluckhohn, *loc. cit.*

PSYCHIATRY AND SOCIOLOGY

Psychoanalysis gave sociology a decisive change of direction because it provided detailed records of the interrelations between individuals and social organizations. As a result, institutions can be studied from an entirely new approach, i.e., what instinctive impulses, what ego interests, and what type of guilt feelings do they provide outlets for?[43]

While psychiatrists worked in state hospitals, they were not concerned with the patient-society relationships, except to keep patients confined if they were potentially dangerous to society or to protect them from social neglect. Their role was to administer the public institutions, and their responsibility was to manage social pressures and maneuver politically in such a way as to procure enough money to provide staff and upkeep sufficient to achieve the ends stated above. The job nevertheless made the psychiatrist a kind of sociologist.

Psychiatrists in private practice have shown little professional interest in the problems of social groups. Their field of activity is restricted chiefly to a microscopic study of the individual personality, who is related dynamically to the systematic social life out of which he comes.[44]

---

[43] H. Hartman, "Psychoanalysis and Sociology," in *Psychoanalysis Today*, ed. by Sandor Lorand (New York: International Universities Press, 1944), pp. 326–334.

[44] F. Alexander, "Roundtable Discussion: Section on Culture and Personality," *Am. J. Orthopsychiat.*, 8: 31–50 (Jan., 1938).

During World War II, however, many psychiatrists found that in order to protect and improve the mental health of members of the armed forces, they had to understand the relations between the individual and the institution of which he suddenly found himself a part. The Neuropsychiatry Consultants Division of the Office of the Surgeon General co-operated closely with the research section of the Information and Education Division of the War Department under Doctors Charles Dollard and Sam Stauffer. Sociologic opinion surveys, which they made, provided physicians with valuable information for a better understanding of the military psychiatric patient and with indications of the need for preventive psychiatric measures. In military service, the chief accomplishments of preventive psychiatry were concerned with groups.

Interchange of ideas and collaboration between sociology and psychiatry are increasing. The interests of these two sciences are inseparable, although their studies are made from different points of reference. Sociology regards the institution as establishing the statutes and regulating the relations of persons to one another.[45] Psychiatry regards the institution as a creation of the individual to satisfy his needs. Sociology is interested in groups of people; psychiatry is interested in the individual.

Both sciences are vitally concerned with the social

[45] T. Parsons, "Propaganda and Social Control," *Psychiatry*, 5: 551–572 (Nov., 1942).

problems of our times. As an illustration, the psychiatrist observes the effect of our changing family structure upon the personality development of the child. The sociologist believes that we cannot leave changes in social organizations, including the family, merely to chance.[46] From both points of view a reconstruction of the family is indicated: from the point of view of the psychiatrist this must originate in the individual; in the thinking of the sociologist the responsibility belongs to society.

Their different methods of approach to the problems are not antithetical but complemental and supplemental. The behavior of an individual in a given social structure can be evaluated rightly only as we know about two things. The first, the personality and its maturity, is the psychiatrist's chief interest. The second, the demands of the social unit and how they modify the individual's behavior, is the sociologist's chief interest. If social reconstruction is to be achieved, it can come about only as a result of a knowledge of both the personality and the social structure in which it functions. The findings of either may be sterile if considered alone.

Many intriguing problems are soluble only by the cooperation of sociology and psychiatry. What additional light does a knowledge of unconscious motivation throw on various types of social behavior? To what degree do institutions express the psychic tendencies of the individual members of society? What are the psycho-

---

[46] E. L. Koos, *Families in Trouble* (New York: King's Crown Press, 1946).

dynamic and interpersonal relationships in leadership and how do these influence the group? The answers to these and many other questions can come only from joint study and investigation by sociologists and psychiatrists. A potentially rich harvest is there for both.

PSYCHIATRY AND RELIGION

Whatever the organization of belief and ceremony, religious experience is so importantly significant that the psychiatrist must often consider its role in the treatment of his patients.

Unfortunately a few religious leaders have recently made a great effort to set up a straw man of conflict between psychiatry and religion. They have tried to show that psychiatry, specifically psychoanalysis, is antireligious and destructive of religious faith. But to the astute observer of the relationship, psychiatry is no more pro- or antireligious than is surgery. Some psychiatrists are strongly religious and others are atheists, just as are other kinds of doctors, educators, laborers. Their individual remarks for or against religion or their interpretations of it should not be construed as being a generally accepted or official opinion of their professional group.

Because of the misunderstanding that seemed to be prevalent, a group of psychiatrists recently made a statement, unique in the history of psychiatry, regarding the relationship between religion and psychiatry. The content of this statement is not so important as the fact that many psychiatrists agreed to its release in order to help clarify the thinking of many people. The formulation, agreed to by approximately one hundred members of the Group for the Advancement of Psychiatry, was as follows:

For centuries, religion and medicine have been closely related. Psychiatry as a branch of medicine has been so closely related to religion that at times the two were almost inseparable. As science developed, however, medicine and religion assumed distinctive roles in society, but they continue to share the common aim of human betterment. This also holds true for that method of psychiatry known as psychoanalysis.

We, as members of the Group for the Advancement of Psychiatry believe in the dignity and the integrity of the individual. We believe that a major goal of treatment is the progressive attainment of social responsibility. We recognize as of crucial significance, the influence of the home upon the individual and the importance of ethical training in the home. We also recognize the important role religion can play in bringing about an improved emotional and moral state.

The methods of psychiatry aim to help patients achieve health in their emotional lives so that they may live in harmony with society and with its standards. We believe that there is no conflict between psychiatry and religion. In the practice of his profession, the competent psychiatrist will therefore always be guided by this belief.

As indicated in this statement, the aims of religion and psychiatry have many common points. "Prophetic religion and scientific medicine meet in the fact that both of them are built on *faith*, share *curiosity* and subordinate themselves to necessary *discipline*." [47]

The goals of psychiatry and religion are closely allied, and indeed some areas overlap. As stated by one religious leader:

Both [psychiatry and religion] recognize the worth of the individual. Both are concerned with the resolution of conflicts and integration of the personality. Both are desirous of achieving for people an adequate security. Both are aware of the high potentiality of emotional involvement in all problems of life. Both are aware that effective living involves social adjustment. Both strive to give meaning and value to the life of the individual.[48]

There would be no disagreement with these remarks by psychiatrists.

There is need for the co-operation of clergymen and psychiatrists. Pastors should learn to recognize when the persons who come to them for help are mentally ill and need psychiatric consultation. Psychiatrists should recognize the powerful emotional support that many individuals derive from their religious faith. In some emotional crises, a religious mentor may be able to provide more important support than can the psychiatrist. There need be no conflict as to when each can serve

---

[47] J. L. Liebman, "Medicine and Religion," sermon delivered at AMA Convention, *J.A.M.A.*, 35: 1479 (Aug. 23, 1947).

[48] H. L. Bowman, "Mental Hygiene in Relation to Religion," *Mental Hyg.*, 20: 177–188 (April, 1936).

best in the resolution of problems. The pastor and priest deal entirely with conscious material. The psychiatrist begins with conscious material but, in addition, sets out to find the unconscious sources of inner conflict. Nor should there be qualms or resentment because psychiatrists turn their scientific microscope upon the role of religion in the life of the individual. It is their scientific duty and responsibility to learn how the personality utilizes its internal equipment and the external environment to find "peace of mind." Despite the few irrationally prejudiced remarks and articles written by those who would stir up antipathies, psychiatrists and clergy are working together, and understanding and borrowing support from each other.

An article [49] in a new journal issued for the first time last August by the Institute of Pastoral Care of the Massachusetts General Hospital states that the role of both the clergyman and the psychiatrist "is largely that of a catalytic agent." The author presents various reasons why the co-operation of these two professions is desirable and necessary and gives an outline of the procedure of co-operation:

The clergyman should become alert to danger signals of personality difficulty. The psychiatrist should be available to confirm or dismiss probability of incipient illness.

---

[49] R. J. Fairbanks, "Cooperation Between Clergy and Psychiatrist," *J. Pastoral Care (Mass. Gen. Hosp.)*, 1: 5–11 (Aug., 1947).

The pastor should be able to render psychiatric "first aid."
Cross referral (more rare for the psychiatrist to refer to the
pastor) is desirable.

The minister can often helpfully interpret psychiatry to the
parishioner-patient, and the psychiatrist can interpret the
role of religion.

The minister can sometimes interpret religion (or more
often a denomination) to the psychiatrist.

Co-operation is specially valuable in dealing with conflicts
involving values. Religion in its higher forms is a philosophy
of moral, aesthetic, and dedicatory values.

The pastor's contact with patient can fit into "multiple relationships therapy," controlled mosaic of interaction.

The pastor can provide supportive therapy temporarily,
group therapy with parish organizations. Insight therapy
from minister would require more training than most of
them have.

Preventive therapy needs, deserves, and invites the co-
operation of all professions in releasing extreme tension
among adolescents, establishing healthy interpersonal relationships among children, and recognizing the role of the
leader model.

A clergyman has for years supervised theological
students in short internships at the Elgin, Illinois, State
Hospital. A course in religion is given by the chaplains for
the psychiatric residents in the Menninger Foundation
School of Psychiatry. Through the Council for Clinical
Training, many theological schools now arrange for

45

internships for their students in psychiatric hospitals.[50] A course in psychiatry is given in the Catholic University of America. The Federal Council of Churches of Christ in America has taken active leadership in presenting mental hygiene to clergymen in special conferences. Not only is there no basic conflict between religion and psychiatry, but there is an increasing appreciation of their many common aims and of the necessity for their co-operation.

In reviewing all these relationships, it becomes obvious that psychiatry is not as yet well integrated with any of these fields. This is because none of them have been clearly defined—nor perhaps can they be in the near future. All the social sciences, like psychiatry, are rapidly increasing their funds of knowledge and the applications of that knowledge. All are only in the process of becoming acquainted with what the others have to offer. Even to the casual observer it is apparent that they are becoming more closely allied, contributing more to each other, and have overlapping interests in many areas.

Psychiatry has made so much progress in the relatively short period of fifty years, that one is tempted to speculate about its potential role in the future. Dr. Alan Gregg, Director of Medical Sciences of the Rockefeller Foundation, speaking specifically of the relationship of psychiatry to medicine, suggests that the historian of medi-

---

[50] These were well described by Howard Whitman, "New Horizons for Your Pastor," *Woman's Home Companion*, Nov., 1947, p. 32.

cine during the last fifty years might well employ the Psalmist's prophecy, "The stone which the builders rejected, the same has become the headstone of the corner." [51] In discussing the future of psychiatry, Dr. Lester Evans [52] of the Commonwealth Fund, who is not a psychiatrist, speculated on its role from another point of view: "Psychiatry or the knowledge coming from the psychological and psychiatric fields might well replace biochemistry as the 'pace setter' in medicine in the period into which we are now moving." All of us in psychiatry modestly hope that the trend expressed in the speculations of Doctors Gregg and Evans may be realized, not only in medicine, but in all the other fields to which psychiatry has much to contribute and from which it has even more to learn.

---

[51] A. Gregg, "A Critique of Psychiatry," *Am. J. Psychiatry*, 101: 287–291 (Nov., 1944).

[52] Personal communication, Sept. 8, 1947.

Chapter 2

Psychoanalytic Psychiatry: Its Contribution to the Understanding of Behavior

THE USE of the term "psychoanalytic psychiatry" * implies that there are other brands or types of this science. Historically this is true. As indicated in the previous lecture, there were and still are those who approach psychiatry as if all mental illness could be treated as an organic nervous disease problem. There are others who are quite content with practicing a psychiatry of description, merely noting the constellation of symptoms and classifying them without seeking to understand the meaning of the illness or giving specific treatment. Psychoanalytic psychiatry is synonymous with dynamic psychiatry, and its fund of knowledge dates from the truly great discoveries of Freud, which began in 1890. It is the only psychiatry that has formulated theories of anatomy and of the physiology of the personality.

Though some persons express disagreement with some of Freud's observations and conclusions, they do so in most instances without having carefully studied his original reports. Even psychiatrists who are critical have accepted and obviously utilize much more of Freud's contribution than they seem to recognize. There are, of

---

* An attempt to explain much of the content of psychoanalytic psychiatry in simple terms has been made by Munro Leaf and the author in *You and Psychiatry* (New York: Chas. Scribner's Sons, 1948).

course, others who are poorly informed about the progress in this field and are either ignorant of, or blind to, the many changes in the theoretical concepts postulated, altered, or added, not only by Freud himself but by many of the followers of the school that grew around his studies.

Regardless of our personal or scientific opinions of Freud and his work, many of us feel that through his stimulus psychiatry was given a new birth. It was converted from a purely descriptive science, largely preoccupied with psychoses, into a dynamic, rational system capable of serving as a basis for interpreting psychopathology. Such interpretations are applicable to the acts of everyday behavior as well as to the great variety of human illnesses described as neurotic reactions.

It may be helpful for the sake of orientation to amplify the meaning of the word *psychoanalysis*. Psychoanalysis was the term employed by Freud initially to refer to a method of treatment. It is still used in this sense to identify a technique that is applicable in a very limited number of personality disturbances. In the process of using it as a treatment, however, Freud accumulated an enormous amount of material. As he attempted to evaluate and classify his data, he developed a psychological theory. As a consequence, when one speaks of psychoanalysis, he may refer to this psychological theory. The term "psychoanalysis" also refers to a research technique. Obtaining data by a process of clearing away, stratum by stratum, the abnormal psychic material is a process

Freud likened to the excavation of a buried city. In both instances the find was apt to prove surprising, and emphatically so in the case of psychoanalytic investigation. All three of these features, namely, a method of treatment, a psychological theory, and an investigative procedure, have continued to be characteristics of the total process of psychoanalysis.

In presenting certain features of psychoanalysis one must recognize that there are parts that can be understood completely only in the frame of the whole theory. In presenting a discussion of some specific elements, one is keenly aware of the risk of giving a totally inadequate conception of the composite whole.

I shall attempt to present in an extremely condensed fashion four of the major areas of psychoanalytic psychiatry that contribute most to the understanding of behavior: the psychosexual stages of development, the anatomy of personality in terms of the conscious and unconscious, personality physiology in terms of the Id, Ego, and Super-Ego, and, finally, some examples of the defense mechanisms used by the Ego to maintain its equilibrium.

PSYCHOSEXUAL DEVELOPMENT [1]

One of the most significant discoveries of psychoanalysis was that the events of infancy and babyhood are all-important in shaping the personality or character of

---

[1] S. Freud, *Three Contributions to the Theory of Sex* (4th ed., New York: Nervous and Mental Disease Publishing Co., 1930), pp. 35–60.

the individual. Psychoanalysis turned the spotlight, perhaps, better, the telescope, on this area of development and has shown without question or doubt that it is during these early years that the basic personality structure and patterns of behavior are laid down. It is during this period that the groundwork is laid for later mental health or ill health. Since this experience occurs during a period for which the adult has amnesia, he is completely unable to explain certain attitudes or behavior in himself.

Freud's study and evaluation of the data he had gained in the treatment of his patients indicated to him that there were definite stages in infant and child personality growth and psychosexual development.[2]

With the introduction of the term "psychosexual," additional explanation is in order. One of the most frequent criticisms of psychoanalysis is that it is too much occupied with sex. Critics are unaware, however, of the fact that to Freud the term "sex" meant far more than genital activity. It included all forms of physical gratification. Moreover, few of these critics know that every psychiatric patient under intensive psychological treatment always brings up this subject himself. The treatment of patients led to the discovery that seeking for gratification is an instinctive drive in every person and cannot be ignored because of prudishness any more than can any other instinctive need. Even as the term is used

---

[2] A clear, easy-reading presentation of psychosexual development is given by I. Hendrick, *Facts and Theories of Psychoanalysis* (New York: Alfred A. Knopf, 1934), pp. 29–62.

in America, sex is one of the basic and all-pervasive motivations in life. Furthermore, everyone has some minor or major difficulties concerned with sexual life at various crucial periods of development—during adolescence, at marriage, or at other times when adjustment must be made to associates or spouse. Sexual maladjustment is accepted, even by nonpsychoanalytic psychiatrists, as a major causative factor in mental illness. In any case, the misunderstanding is due both to semantic differences and to the suppression and repression of this basic human interest and activity. The result has been much resistance to the initial acceptance of psychoanalysis both as a body of knowledge and as a treatment technique. Incidentally, the American cultural taboo against discussion of this instinctual need is a significant factor in the high incidence of neuroses.

Growing up entails changing from a little animal concerned only with his own physical processes into a social being cognizant of relationships between himself and other people. This change starts in the first year of life. Very early the inherent internal forces within the child, namely, his will to live, to express himself, and to find gratification, must be integrated with his surroundings, his environment, his parents, his siblings, and the external world. It is through the initial and early experiences in the family that the child learns to relate himself to people and to develop certain techniques by which he accomplishes this.

When the infant is born into the world, we can be sure

PSYCHOANALYTIC PSYCHIATRY

that he has no interest except selfishly to gratify his own cravings. He has certain instincts at birth, and the demand to satisfy these is his only motive in life. In his early months the infant gives nothing to anyone else; he makes no attempt to please anyone; in short, he is interested only in receiving what he wants. One may say that he follows the path of gaining all the pleasure he can and so far as possible avoiding displeasure and pain in any form. This pattern of behavior follows what is known as the "pleasure-pain principle": [3] All effort is directed toward obtaining pleasure and avoiding pain, regardless of consequences. The term "pain" refers not only to physical suffering but also to every other sort of displeasure, unhappiness, and discomfort.

It is only after some years that the child begins to apply what is known as the "reality principle," [4] namely, the acceptance of a limited amount of pain or unhappiness or dissatisfaction because of the promise of more gratification in the future. It is one of the changes that must occur in order for the child to become an adult psychologically.

During the first three, four, or five years of life the child has three experiences that are of paramount interest to him and through which he formulates his relations to those about him. Continuing through most of his first

---

[3] S. Freud, "Formulations Regarding the Two Principles of Mental Functioning," in *Collected Papers* (London: Hogarth Press, 1934), IV, 13–21.

[4] S. Freud, *Beyond the Pleasure Principle* (London: Hogarth Press, 1922).

year is his interest in and his gratification from nursing (sucking). This is his chief contact with the external world and with those about him, and it serves as his chief source of satisfaction.

Toward the end of this year a new interest appears. Through the efforts of his parents to encourage his control of his excretions, the child's attention becomes focused on those processes. They become his chief bodily interest and in some degree replace the previously primary interest in using his mouth.

Between the second and third year the child's interest turns to curiosity about his or her sexual organs and their function, how they differ from those of others. Concurrent with and related to the interest in this new area of physical gratification, is a new type of relationship to his parents and siblings.

The child passes imperceptibly from one phase to another in his development; no lines of demarkation separate one period from another. Nevertheless, it is possible to outline the various characteristics in each of these stages. The evolution of growth through these periods is referred to as psychosexual development. It is psychical development because it has to do with forms of psychological gratification. It is sexual development because it concerns various parts of the body that serve as sources of gratification. It will be apparent that the word "sexual" in this connection is obviously a much more inclusive term than laymen ordinarily consider it.

THE ORAL STAGE

For a period of at least the infant's first year, sometimes longer, his chief interest in life centers around an event that occurs every three or four hours—his feeding. Not only does nursing provide satisfaction through the process of sucking and by ending the discomfort of hunger, but it is also usually a time for cuddling. Anything that happens with this frequency, with resultant gratification or lack of it, must in many ways affect subsequent attitudes concerned with the taking-in or receiving tendencies of the individual.

While the food itself serves as a source of gratification, the child also gets great satisfaction from the procedure of sucking. Carefully made studies show that children who have been bottle-fed are much more likely to be thumbsuckers than those who are breast-fed, the explanation being that the breast-fed baby usually nurses about fifteen minutes and the bottle-fed baby about five minutes. To make up the difference the bottle-fed baby often develops the habit of sucking his finger or a pacifier to obtain additional satisfaction. One of the most important elements in this feeding difference is the amount of coddling or affection that the child receives from the parent. Too often the bottle is propped up and the baby left to himself during feeding time.

There are two distinct phases in this "oral stage" of development, a sucking phase and a biting phase. It is presumed that in the earlier phase of sucking, the child regards the breast as part of himself. He makes no distinction between the breast as part of his mother and the parts of his own body. It is only after weeks or perhaps months that the child recognizes the breast as an object that can be taken away from him. As he grows and demands more food and at the same time is developing teeth, the mother is made well aware of the baby's frequent inclination to bite. Particularly is this true when the milk may not be forthcoming as rapidly as the child wishes it; in his impatience he bites the nipple. The biting is the result of frustration, the expression of a temporary resentment because the child is thwarted in gaining the oral satisfaction he wishes.

Many hang-overs of this oral phase are expressed in normal adulthood.[5] Our responses to our first experience in receiving become the prototype for our techniques of receiving, obtaining, and taking in later life. It is probable that the traits of optimism and dependence are related to this period. Certain character traits in the adult are traceable to unsatisfactory experiences in this period of life, particularly impatience, hastiness, and restlessness. The "biter" becomes the argumentative, vitriolic, and sarcastic adult.

----

[5] Because psychoanalysts regard these early experiences as extremely important in the formation of character, they have indicated by the terms "oral character" and "anal character" certain personality constellations seen in some adults. The "oral character" is well described by K. Abraham, *Selected Papers* (London: Hogarth Press, 1927), p. 393, and by O. Fenichel, *Outline of Clinical Psychoanalysis* (New York: W. W. Norton & Co., 1934), pp. 431–434.

Numerous traits are directly related to the oral process itself, as expressed by those individuals whose chief interest in life is eating in spite of gains in weight and in those who are Epicureans of the first order, to whom eating is the most enjoyable activity. Smoking is another oral gratification: the inhalation of smoke gives satisfaction related to that of sucking. Other examples are pipe, cigar, pencil, and gum chewing. An obvious expression of oral gratification is seen in the unfortunate immature individual who in later life substitutes for the earlier bottle of milk one which contains alcohol.

THE ANAL STAGE

In practice, this stage of development begins whenever the parents initiate training. It is now believed that the toilet training of the child should not begin until some time in the second year. Unfavorable personality reactions are more likely to develop when it is started during the first year, for then the parent imposes a regime upon the insufficiently mature child. In that case, for a period of many months or even a year or two, the child is placed on the toilet at regular intervals several times a day. It is the intention of the parent to gain the child's co-operation by focusing his attention upon this particular procedure. It can be readily understood why any ceremony of this sort, so often repeated, and upon which the parent places so much emphasis, often emotional as well as physical, becomes of considerable importance to the child.

Certain elements in the procedure assume special significance to the child. Very early he learns that this business of urinating and defecating is a method he can use to gain love and approval, or to revenge himself and show determination. In other words, he soon finds that it is one way in which he, an infant, can have power over the adult. Every parent is familiar with the situation in which the child will not "do his duty" regardless of persuasion, pleading, or even threats. Then, as soon as he is removed from the toilet, he performs. In this way the child can express his own desires, his disapproval or hostility toward the parent and toward the idea of control. On the other hand, parents are equally familiar with the situation in which the child responds to pleas to "be a big girl" or "a big boy"; thus, learns that by doing as the parents wish, he or she can gain their love and approval.

One can also observe that the child soon becomes intensely interested not only in the process but in the product. It is literally his first creation. One can observe further that, early in his training, the child derives a very definite gratification through either the expulsion or later the retention of this product. In either case he has a sense of omnipotence, of power that is entirely his. Response to the parental emphasis on regularity and cleanliness serves to instill these characteristics in varying degrees into the personality.

In the adult, the residual expressions of the training and experience in the anal phase of infancy are even more varied than the oral expressions.[6] This probably occurs because, with increasing age, there is increased suppression as well as repression of conscious interest in this procedure. Fundamentally this experience is the prototype of our technique of giving, and thus an important relationship between ourselves and the world. It is undoubtedly related to such character traits as perseverance, persistence, orderliness, cleanliness, and conscientiousness in one's duties. On the other hand, some of the more disagreeable personality characteristics are related to this period. It gave us our first lessons in being stubborn, in refusing to co-operate. Obstinacy has its origin in this phase of an individual's life, along with parsimony, particularly as this becomes avarice and miserliness. Toilet training gave us our first experience in how to be mean to our parents—later, to other people. Not only does the child learn that he can offend or hurt his parents by refusing to co-operate, but he can make matters much worse by soiling himself. Even the layman is familiar with such suggestive expressions as "mud slinging," "whitewashing," "painting things red," "messing things up,"

---

[6] The so-called "anal character" was described originally by E. Jones, "Anal Erotic Character Traits," in *Papers on Psychoanalysis* (New York: William Wood & Co., 1923), pp. 680–704. It was also described by Abraham, *op. cit.*, p. 370, and by Fenichel, *op. cit.*, pp. 426–431. The writer attempted a detailed breakdown of the direct and sublimated expressions of the anal period in "Characterologic and Symptomatic Expressions Related to the Anal Phase of Psychosexual Development," *Psychoanalyt. Quart.*, 12: 161–193 (April, 1943).

all of which are polite references to the sadistic tendencies that result from this training.

GENITAL STAGE

The child becomes curious about his own sexual organs in the third year. He discovers differences between himself and his sisters and his parents. The objectively observing parent knows when the child discovers his genital area and fingers it (which is referred to as "infantile masturbation"), or enjoys the stimulation of this area through bouncing, rocking, and other types of play.

Even the young child soon becomes aware that genital manipulation is taboo. All too often his innocent questions are met by rebuff on the part of his parents. As a result, most children learn early to believe that all things sexual are "naughty" or "dirty." Even more disturbing to the child is the attitude that they are "forbidden." Too often parents do not realize that interest in the genitals and sexual differences is a natural, normal phase of development.

Acquaintance with sex differences is intimately bound up with the child's attempt to orientate toward his father as a man and toward his mother as a woman. It is at this time that every little child has a conflict in relating himself to his or her parents. Extensive evidence for this has been gained from the psychoanalytic investigation of many, many individuals. The little boy initially craves the entire attention and love of his mother but recognizes some sort of competition with the father.[7] In a normal, healthy solution of his dilemma, he forms a new part of his personality, the Super-Ego (which we will discuss later), which enables him to identify himself with his father as an ally rather than as a competitor. By so doing he makes what is termed a masculine identification. To solve his problem he imitates his father in manners, dress, and behavior. Similarly the little girl goes through the same conflict in relation to sharing her father with her mother, which ends, in normal development, when she identifies herself with her mother and thus adopts a pattern for feminine identification.

In summarizing these psychosexual stages of development, it should again be pointed out that these events are important in that, first, they determine the methods by which the child relates himself to his environment and particularly to the people in it; second, they are the basis of techniques by which the child obtains gratification. In all three phases, basic character traits are initiated and patterns developed that largely determine the characteristics of that personality as an adult.

THE UNCONSCIOUS

The second major contribution of psychoanalytic psychiatry to the understanding of behavior is a concept of

---

[7] This conflict, known as the "Oedipus situation," has been described by Hendrick, *op. cit.*, pp. 49–52; K. A. Menninger, *The Human Mind* (3d ed., New York: Alfred A. Knopf, 1945), pp. 306–317; K. Stephen, *Psychoanalysis and Medicine: A Study of the Wish to Fall Ill* (New York: Macmillan Co., 1933), pp. 162–189.

63

the anatomy of the personality as being divided into a conscious and an unconscious portion. None of us have clear recollections of those experiences in infancy that occurred during psychosexual development. Thus none of us have any real knowledge of the basis of many of our most outstanding personality traits—honesty or dishonesty, sociability, selfishness or unselfishness, and so forth. The average individual usually believes that he knows why he does all that he does. Sometimes, however, his explanations for his attitudes and behavior are so shallow that he himself may question their validity. Occasionally he may admit that he does not know just why he does a certain thing or why he takes a certain point of view. Human behavior is complex, and the average person has no explanation why one individual has a persistent fear of crowded places or another has frank delusions. The same would puzzle the psychiatrist without a theory of the existence of a major part of the personality—the unconscious—that motivates much of our behavior.

Originally, as the explanation of neurotic behavior, Freud [8] postulated the existence of a large area in the individual's personality that was not under voluntary control. In his early definition of the theory he tried to explain neurotic symptoms as resulting from the interaction of forces, some of which obviously arose from a deep, unrecognized layer of the personality and others of which stemmed from a conscious level of the person-

---

[8] S. Freud, *The Ego and the Id* (London: Hogarth Press, 1927), pp. 9–18.

ality. In order to develop a functional concept, he made a topographical division of the personality into a conscious and an unconscious system. The chief source of symptoms was the conflict between the forces resident in each system. "The outcome of this conflict depended upon the economic relationship between these two sets of forces, yet the sum of the two psychic forces could practically always be considered constant." [9] This simple theory was later amplified by Freud himself into a much more complicated one in order that he might take into account many additional factors, both within and without the personality, that he believed determined behavior.

By definition, the psychiatrist regards the unconscious as a large region of the mind that is inaccessible to conscious awareness by ordinary means of questioning or self-examination. In it are contained the inherited and racial trends. This region of the mind contains the basic energy drives. In the very small infant they are allowed free expression without restraint and without modification. As the child grows up, the primitive expressions of these drives have to be molded, cloaked, and controlled, but they remain the sources of energy. The unconscious also contains the no longer consciously remembered learning experiences of infancy and early childhood as well as all the associations established at that time.

---

[9] S. Ferenczi, "Freud's Influence on Medicine," in *Psychoanalysis Today*, ed. by Sandor Lorand (New York: Covici-Friede, 1933), p. 6.

The unconscious cannot be demonstrated like the brain, for it is not an anatomical unit. It is a concept whereby behavior can be explained. There is much evidence to support the premise of such a functional portion of the personality, perhaps the most convincing of which can be demonstrated in the process we call hypnosis. Hypnosis is a form of suggestion by which certain individuals can be placed in a trancelike state, subject to the control of the hypnotist. In this state of mind an individual may recall incidents or remember facts that he is not able to recall normally. During this trance the hypnotist can make suggestions to be carried out after the person has emerged from the hypnotic state and without the person's recalling that these acts were suggested to him.

Another very common type of evidence of the existence of the unconscious is one's dreams. Some popular opinion may regard them as nonsensical and meaningless. Nevertheless, scientifically they are recognized as a kind of thought process, which is specific for the dreamer. They always have a significant relationship to the thought process of his conscious life. The dream is a production of the unconscious part of the mind that is censored and altered before reaching the conscious part. It is usually so disguised that the average individual cannot recognize its true meaning.

Further evidence that a portion of the personality is not under voluntary control is the slip of speech. We say one thing but mean another. In an unguarded moment, when the conscious censor of the personality is "off duty," the slip of speech occurs and we express the opposite of what we intended to say. Very closely related to this type of psychological phenomena is the common experience of forgetting something that we know we know but cannot remember. The recall of a person's name, a name with which we are quite familiar, is sometimes unsuccessful, even after a special effort to remember it. It is often possible to demonstrate that in such instances, because of some unpleasant association, we do not want to recall the name, and in spite of great effort to do so the name continues to elude the conscious mind.

Recall of forgotten experiences under special conditions is another evidence of the unconscious. Only under certain circumstances can we recapture the memory of them. This is a most important phenomenon, however, because certain long-forgotten infantile and childhood experiences must be recalled in the effective treatment of some mental illnesses.

The psychoanalytic concept regards the unconscious as a powerful force in the life of every individual and not as an inert group of discarded experiences or associations. The unconscious is present at birth and exists throughout life, always remaining primitive and infantile. In other words, it is the conscious part of us that matures while the unconscious remains the same from babyhood to old age. Not only does it contain inherited instinctual drives, but it also receives many of the unacceptable interests, desires, and experiences that we must repress, that is, exclude from our conscious personality. Into the unconscious of every individual must go the erotic satisfactions of infancy, the forbidden hostile feelings toward parents and siblings, and many other unsocial wishes and even behavior that the mature adult personality cannot accept as a part of his conscious life.

THE ID, EGO, SUPER-EGO RELATIONSHIP

The division of the personality into conscious and unconscious levels does not completely explain human emotions, thought, and behavior. A further elaboration of the psychoanalytic theory describes these conscious and unconscious regions as having three functional and interrelated systems, each of which has certain characteristics and functions. Each is dependent to some degree on the others, the Id, the Ego, the Super-Ego.[10]

The Id, which is the sum total of the personality at birth, is primitive and exists entirely in the unconscious. By primitive we mean that it is animallike, uncivilized, uncultured. It is the "it" in all of us that accounts for the demanding, selfish, inconsiderate part of all of us. If one were to verbalize its continuous theme song, it would be "it wants."

At birth, there is no Ego. As the personality develops,

---

[10] The first description of these concepts was given by Freud. It was originally published in 1923 and republished in 1927 under the title of *The Ego and the Id*. The interested reader will find a simple, clear description of the functions and interrelationships in Hendrick, *op. cit.*, pp. 141–151, and in E. Jones, *Psychoanalysis* (New York: J. Cape & H. Smith, 1929), pp. 35–41.

that conscious portion of ourselves (although part of it remains unconscious) that acts as an intermediary between the Id and the external world is called the Ego. In it reside our conscious storehouse of knowledge and the intellectual capacities to choose and to judge and to think. Its theme song, both to the Id and to the world, is "I will" or "I will not."

The Super-Ego is a third portion of the personality that grows with us. It is our internal policeman; it functions as the judge and the critic; it embraces what we call conscience. The phrase which characterizes its advice to the Ego is "you must not."

This theory of the interworking of these three parts of the personality gives us a rational basis for understanding human behavior. These do not represent physical parts of the brain but rather are functional systems, and the sum total of their expression is behavior.

The Id. The Id is that portion of the personality that constitutes most of the unconscious region. It makes up the whole of the personality at birth. The Id remains unrefined throughout life and is that part of the individual referred to popularly as "the animal in man." It has no regard for morals; it never learns or acquires what we think of as intelligence. It never "grows up"; it changes little from birth to adulthood except through the additions of certain experiences that the conscious part of the individual refuses to keep in its own house and so forces into the domain of the Id. Its only rule of existence is to seek pleasure and avoid pain, regardless of consequences.

Its function, if we may call it such, is to supply the psychic energy that the person uses in life, the will to live. Freud [11] was sufficiently discerning to distinguish two directions or aims of motivation in the expenditure of psychological energy. He identified these as "instincts," using the term to refer to an unconscious, impelling drive toward a particular type of behavior. He believed that these two drives were related to each other and that, under ideal circumstances of adjustment, they would interact in such a way as to neutralize the overt, primitive expressions of each other. One of these instincts impels the individual toward aggressive, destructive, or hostile behavior. The other impels the individual toward erotic, constructive, or affectionate behavior.

Both of these instincts or drives are manifest in the behavior of everyone. The relationships established by one person with other people and with objects, as well as all forms of behavior, can be identified as expressions of these two motivating pressures. As suggested, the ideal adjustment implies a fusion of the aggressive and affectionate elements within the personality. When sufficiently blended with a constructive, affectionate instinct, the aggressive element loses its hostile, destructive element.[12] When there is a failure in the fusion, one sees the direct expressions of hate and destruction.

---

[11] S. Freud, *Three Contributions to the Theory of Sex;* "Instincts and Their Vicissitudes," in *Collected Papers*, IV, 60–83.

[12] This is the main theme of the book by my brother Karl and Jeanetta Lyle Menninger, *Love Against Hate* (New York: Harcourt, Brace & Co., 1942).

In our culture the expressions of these drives are expected to be modified, directed, or deflected into acceptable social behavior. At best, however, the conscious ego can exert only a somewhat superficial control, so that one's ideas and action may give minor and major evidences of the predominance of either constructive or destructive impulses in a particular personality at a particular time. These drives may be vented or invested externally or turned in toward the self.[13] In their external expressions they are constantly modified by the environmental situation. The resulting changes in the balance of the forces within the individual and between him and the outside world are the dynamic factors in personality development.

A recognition of the presence of these drives as dynamic forces is important, but even more important is an understanding of their evolution. This evolution follows a similar pattern in everyone. The drives are modified by parental training, by developmental experiences, and by the many other contacts with the external world. In the infant most of the time the two antagonistic drives are so fused as to neutralize each other. Their energy is directed almost completely toward himself. As the world begins to intrude into his life with its irritations and frustrations, he expresses hostile aggression toward it. Through growth and training, if given love, the individual learns

---

[13] Evidences and types of aggression turned on the self have been elaborated by my brother Karl in *Man Against Himself* (New York: Harcourt, Brace & Co., 1938).

to merge the hostile with the erotic instinctual drives in order to react with toleration, and under suitable conditions to return affection. Some of the initial irritations he may absorb; others he may elude; still others he will change with his acquisition of experience and knowledge so that they cease to be irritating. As the child grows, more and more of his energy is directed away from himself and invested in the objects or the people he encounters in his environment. His reaction to them may be either hostile and aggressive or erotic and affectionate, or it may be neutral.

Individuals vary in the success with which they are able to deflect the direction of this energy from themselves to the external world. Some retain a considerable investment of the erotic drive in themselves, as manifested in many expressions of self-love. Others retain a considerable degree of investment of the aggressive drive in themselves as manifested in the neuroses, the psychoses, and many other forms of partial and even complete self-destruction.

Ideally, as one reaches psychological maturity, his mastery of the external world presumably makes it unnecessary to direct either the erotic or aggressive drives toward himself. Maturity implies aggressive constructive activity, which brings a gratifying return from appropriate investment. The directing of primitive erotic energy involves giving affection, considerate protection, and confidence to the love object, that is, the mate, who has been selected for his or her own sake and not as a mere substitute for some reluctantly abandoned earlier object, such as a parent. In maturity, the aggressive drive is so merged with the erotic drive as to provide initiative, forcefulness, strength of purpose, competitiveness, decisiveness. It no longer seeks release in any type of self-destruction or handicapping of the self. Sublimated forms of its expression are crusading, militant missionary effort, evangelism, "righteous indignation." Frustrations evoke their expression in normal persons, as do indignities and inhumanities. But ideally, the aggressive force is expressed in pure form only toward threatening or existing danger.

It is apparent then that the power of the Id is a continuous threat to the Ego. When any impulse arising within the Id is blocked in its outlet by the Ego, tension arises and is felt as anxiety.

The Ego. It is the Ego that becomes aware of anxiety because it makes up the bulk of the personality that we refer to as "consciousness." Most of it is conscious, and it represents the thinking, knowing, and feeling part of the person. The Ego begins to develop at birth, in contrast to the Id, which already is well developed at that time. As one learns from experience and gains in knowledge, the Ego expands and grows strong or is weakened, depending on those environmental factors, particularly the parents, that assist in the solution of childhood problems.[14]

---

[14] One of the best discussions of the Ego development in the child is to be found in Anna Freud, *The Ego and the Mechanisms of Defence* (London: Hogarth Press, 1937).

The Ego has numerous functions. It serves as the intermediary between the world, the environment outside the individual, and the inner demands, wishes, and desires that originate in the Id. Thus its first function is to make the primitive drives of the Id conform to the demands of reality. Its guiding rule, so long as it is healthy, is to accept and to modify reality. It has the function of organizing the mental processes in a coherent fashion. It has the responsibility of obtaining gratification and satisfaction from the environment. It must control and govern the crude, though superior strength, of the impulses which come from the deep unconscious. It must mold these so that they are acceptable to the world outside the personality. It must prohibit the direct expression of desires that are self-destructive or that would destroy the environment.

Even when one goes to sleep, the Ego still censors any thought processes that go on, and so one's nocturnal mental activity is forced to express itself in bizarre, distorted forms that we call dreams.

The Ego also controls all voluntary motor functions. A part of the Ego is unconscious, and through this portion of it all repression is carried on, along with other mental mechanisms (to be discussed later), without our being consciously aware of them.

The Super-Ego. The Super-Ego, the third system of the personality, is chiefly unconscious. It begins to develop in the individual during the third or fourth years as a means of partially solving the conflict in orienting himself to his parents. By developing a Super-Ego, the little child borrows strength from his parents through identification with them. He sets up an inhibiting force, a kind of police force within himself, a conscience, which keeps saying to the Ego, "You must not." Within his Super-Ego he has absorbed those standards of control presented to him by parents and teachers.

Thus the Super-Ego is both a conscious and an unconscious conscience, a critic that watches the conscious Ego deal with the strivings of the Id. When the Ego makes poor decisions, including those with which the conscience cannot agree, the Super-Ego criticizes and condemns the Ego. For instance, when one wrongs a friend, he feels remorse in proportion to his understanding of the degree or extent of his aggressions against the friend. His Ego feels guilty and seeks punishment, so that he feels he needs to make restitution. The critical Super-Ego may force him to make excessive efforts toward restitution, which may be expressed in various kinds of self-punishment, self-failure, and self-depreciation.

A knowledge of the interrelations of these three parts or systems of the personality is essential to understanding human behavior. When the equilibrium between them is disturbed, maladjustment results, and the expression of the maladjustment creates symptoms.

The Ego is the intermediary between the Id and Super-Ego and the external world. It must harmonize three powerful forces, that is, the Id, the Super-Ego, and Reality, all of which are potentially stronger than it is.

Sometimes the Ego is unable to conform to reality, that is, the external world; sometimes it is not sufficiently strong to adjust the personality to the demands of the external situation. When it is so threatened, symptoms develop; the soldier in combat frequently develops physical disturbances of his heart or his stomach. Others react by denying the reality situation by the formation of delusions or other types of falsification of the true environmental situation.

Again, if the Ego is sufficiently strong, it either holds the demands and impulses of the Id in check or modifies them into some form of expression that is socially approved. Sometimes the Ego remains loyal to reality, but the primitive wish puts on a masquerade and so disguises itself that it gains expression without the Ego's recognizing it as the forbidden desire. When this occurs, the resulting expression may be a socially approved sublimation or a neurotic symptom. When the Ego is weak, it may permit certain of these primitive impulses to gain direct expression as we see them in psychoses or antisocial behavior.

The Super-Ego dominates the Ego and is critical if the Ego fails to control the Id impulses. It is an inner judge, an unconscious arbiter of our behavior. Its blame leads to the development of feelings of guilt, which lead to self-inflicted punishment, all of which may be entirely an unconscious process.

The equilibrium of the Ego is threatened continuously from all sides. When the Ego weakens or begins to fail in its function, the individual shows the symptom of anxiety. In order to avoid anxiety the Ego develops certain devices that we call "dynamisms," or "mechanisms" that help maintain the equilibrium between these three portions of the personality. They serve as a medium of expression of the Id impulses that can be accepted by external reality. These mechanisms are a necessary part of the functional equipment of the Ego of every person, and they constitute one of the most widely accepted and most helpful portions of psychoanalytic psychiatry.

MENTAL MECHANISMS

A slowly developing conscious Ego can control, guide, and modify the unconscious instinctual energy with only varying degrees of success. There is no one who does not experience an occasional serious maladjustment, nor are any of us completely free of eccentric or unusual traits of character and behavior. Everyone shows neurotic symptoms at one time or another. Complete control of the primitive expressions of energy is not possible all the time and under all circumstances. Psychiatric patients continuously display grossly uncontrolled or only thinly masqueraded expressions of energy that are exaggerations of the pathological behavior of everyday life.

The mental mechanisms are the devices that the personality uses, both in health and in sickness, to channel its unconscious drives. Their expressions are always apparent and conscious, but they originate in the unconscious. Therefore, their stimulus as defenses against tension induced by conflict within the personality is an automatic attempt to control the expression of primitive energy. They are not consciously activated. Once recognized, their action may be modified by a conscious decision to do so. Knowledge of these mechanisms gives us an understanding, not only of illogical behavior and ideation, but also of normal behavior.

At least seventeen different mental mechanisms have been described in psychoanalytic literature,[15] but no classification of these is satisfactory. Some of them are a part of our growth process; thus by introjection we continuously absorb from our environment those ideals, opinions, data, and attitudes that make us what we are. Some mechanisms function primarily as defenses for the Ego against the development of anxiety and are used specifically for this purpose. Repression, mentioned earlier in this discussion, is one of these. The majority of

---

[15] W. Healy and A. F. Bronner, *The Structure and Meaning of Psychoanalysis as Related to Personality and Behavior* (New York: Alfred A. Knopf, 1930), pp. 192–200. This number does not include the special mechanisms of infancy and early childhood described by Anna Freud. She included "denial in phantasy," by which the child defends himself by elaborating his ideas and wishes in phantasy; "denial in word and act," by which he carries out his phantasy through pretense; "restriction of the ego," by which the child constricts or restricts his interest or activity to avoid failure or distress; "identification with the aggressor," through which fear or anxiety is avoided by playing the aggressor; and "a form of altruism," through which surrender is made out as an altruistic act (Anna Freud, *The Ego and the Mechanisms of Defence* [International Psychoanalytic Library, no. 30; London: Hogarth Press, 1937], pp. 73–148).

these mechanisms are utilized both in health and in disease, but all the expressions of a few of them are always symptoms.

It is neither possible nor practical to discuss all these mechanisms [16] in a brief space. Quite deliberately five of the more common have been selected for brief presentation as illustrative examples.

One of the most common mental mechanisms is *sublimation*, the device by which we obtain gratification through the channeling of primitive energy into some type of socially approved activity. Sublimated expressions provide a healthy release of the same instinctual energy that produces symptoms in the sick individual who cannot sublimate or repress it. Although individual capacity for sublimation varies widely, much of the activity of our daily life represents this mechanism. Sublimation is always healthy, and when the individual fails to use it, he invariably displays symptoms. Thus the original aggressive drive, instead of being manifested in its raw forms of hate and destruction, is converted by sublimation into leadership, initiative, and healthy aggressiveness. All of us maintain a reservoir of hostility. In the

---

[16] These mechanisms have been discussed at length in psychoanalytic literature; see S. Freud, *Inhibition, Symptom, and Anxiety* (Stamford, Conn.: The Psychoanalytic Institute, 1927), a technical discussion of the defense mechanisms of regression, repression, isolation, undoing, and reaction formation; Jones, *op. cit.*, pp. 42–47; K. A. Menninger, *The Human Mind*, pp. 281–304, a simple, lucid presentation in popular language of twelve of the mechanisms, with everyday illustrations; I. S. Wechsler, *The Neuroses* (Philadelphia: W. B. Saunders Co., 1929).

79

well-adjusted individual this is drained off through many of our activities, such as a competitive athletic contest or digging in the garden or playing bridge.

Sublimation is exemplified in a major way in the choice of a vocation. Thus the nurse or the kindergarten teacher may resign her desire or hopes for children and find satisfaction in the care of many patients or children; they become the substitutes for children of her own. The primitive desire and gratification obtained in infancy through the infliction of pain or cruelty is sublimated in the butcher, and perhaps in a more refined way in the surgeon. The infantile gratification from the use of power, dominance, independence, and hoarding in the anal stage finds partial outlets in an approved fashion in the banker. Microscopic analysis of all work and play would reveal them as approved outlets for primitive energy and, as such, they represent sublimation.

Rationalization is a second type of mechanism that we all use frequently. Technically speaking, it is the device for explaining plausibly and thus accounting for or justifying certain feelings, ideas, or behavior. The explanation always appears to us a logical one.

All of us at times believe that our mistakes or blunders are the result of fate. We explain our feelings on the basis of the weather. When we do not do something we should, we justify our action; when we want something badly, we find good reasons for getting it. Rationalization does not refer to consciously concocted explanations but rather to apparently honest and logical thought about our attitudes and our behavior. Rationalizations may be used to justify erroneous opinions or ideas. Strong loves and hates, whether they are rational indulgences or frank prejudices, are always supported by what seem to be logical explanations. The drug addict rationalizes the reasons why he must take drugs; the deluded patient explains quite rationally to himself the reasons for his delusions. The alcoholic is sincere in his belief that he began drinking to escape his troubles or his sorrow. In general we defend our position by rationalization.

A specific type of rationalization is called idealization. By this device we avoid being critical of ourselves or of those who are very important to us emotionally. Thus the conceited, exhibitionistic individual consciously is lacking in critical judgment about himself. Lovers have an irrational fondness for each other. Blind hatred, which destroys any critical faculty, is another form of this type of rationalization.

So much of our behavior is motivated by unconscious factors that it is understandable why rationalization is such an important mechanism for our adjustment. We must rationalize in order to explain to ourselves and others why we have certain character traits, why we behave as we do, why we have certain likes and dislikes. Rationalization permits us to believe quite honestly and comfortably that we have the explanation.

Another common mechanism is *displacement*. This is a process by which the emotional value attached to one idea or person is transferred to another idea or person.

The emotional attitude expressed is either out of proportion or unrelated to the object toward which it is directed.

Whenever we misplace the blame or credit for a feeling that we have, we use the mechanism of displacement. Thus the upbraiding of the roommate at the end of a hard day of classes may be a displacement of hostility toward an exacting professor. The excessive lavishing of affection on a dog may be a displacement of desire to lavish affection on some human object. An excess of anger or other emotion over any trivial incident is a displacement from emotion felt about some other situation to which it may or may not be related. When the majority of a class of students fail to make passing grades, the teacher often displaces the responsibility with a belief that the students are lazy, stupid, or eccentric. When parents fail to manage a child, they often express their sense of failure in scolding or whipping the child.

Very often displacement is used in a major way in our lives. Some individuals select as a mate a substitute mother or father and displace their feelings toward their parent in childhood onto the wife or husband. Sometimes we use displacement to keep ourselves blind or to justify our course of action. For instance, not infrequently some of us become so involved in saving the community that our own families are badly neglected. The displacement of our interest and energy often protects us from recognizing the neglect and, perhaps even our resentment, toward our responsibilities to the family. Not infrequently we meet individuals whose maladjustment and dissatisfaction with their lives is taken out on everyone with whom they come in contact, whether this be the wife, the children, the employees, or merely friends.

Displacement is a kind of face-saving device that protects our Egos from seeing their mistakes and that shields us from the unpleasant recognition of our misdirected investments of emotion and interest.

One of the mechanisms that always indicates failing adjustment, even more so than displacement, is *projection*. This is the dynamism by which the individual, in order to protect himself against ideas and wishes that he cannot admit he has, projects them onto another person or object in a more or less disguised form. Even though the expressions of projection may be very mild, their use indicates a failing, or a chronically poor, adjustment.

In the latter case the individual soon acquires a reputation for his tendency to blame others for his own inadequacies. Some people always blame their partners for the mistakes in the card game; they believe they do not get the right breaks; they have the conviction that their employer, their wife, or their associates do not understand them or have been unfair to them. Unjustified suspicions are examples of projection.

By the use of this device the individual always becomes the object of attention, sometimes because of assumed persecution or sometimes by an overevaluation of ability. In either case, he believes himself to be the object of special attention and thus attributes to others an interest in and motives toward himself that are entirely false.

The extreme form of this mechanism is seen in those individuals who may, on the one hand, regard themselves as a special emissary from the Almighty, as a great leader, as the recipient of special God-given abilities, or, on the other hand, as being persecuted by the government, the FBI, the Ku Klux Klan, or some other powerful group.

Finally, another mechanism that is always a manifestation of ill health, is *conversion*. By its use the Ego channels the threatening impulse from the Id into a symbolic expression of pain, distress, or functional disorder in some part of the body. The result always is a physical symptom, either motor or sensory. In this device, as in most of the defense mechanisms, the symptom represents a compromise. The Ego denies the direct expression of the repressed wish, but the symptom is a disguised expression of this wish unrecognized by the Ego.

Minor conversions occur frequently in many of us. In most of us their appearance would not justify the diagnosis of a particular mental illness. We have stomach symptoms because of homesickness. We get a headache from some special frustration. We may develop physical symptoms either in anticipation of or as the result of a situational problem.

Conversion symptoms are most spectacularly illustrated in cases of sudden blindness, loss of voice, paralysis, anesthesia. Most of these develop under acute stress and were rather commonly seen in the combat soldier. Conversion symptoms, however, include all types of physical malfunctioning that have an emotional origin, whether this be of the stomach, heart, lungs, genital system, or other part of the body. Symptoms of this type constitute the complaints of a high percentage of patients seen by family physicians and medical specialists. Therefore, an understanding of the conversion mechanism is extremely important to all medical people.

These five mental mechanisms—sublimation, rationalization, displacement, projection, and conversion—are illustrative of the automatic devices of our mental machinery. These are methods by which the conscious Ego protects itself from the development of anxiety. They are the vehicles and modes of expression, both healthy and unhealthy, of urges or wishes that seek expression from the unconscious. They constitute the psychodynamics of the personality.

SUMMARY

A brief presentation of the psychosexual stages of infantile development, of the theory of the unconscious, of the dynamic systems of Id, Ego, Super-Ego, and of the defense mechanisms permits discussion of only a few of the major points from the body of knowledge of psychoanalytic psychiatry.

Also, the technique of psychoanalytic treatment focuses very special attention on the emotional interrelationships between the patient and the doctor. This interrelationship is now recognized as one of the most important factors in the treatment of any patient by any physician.

There has not been an opportunity to discuss the phenomenon known as ambivalence,[17] namely, that emotional attitudes always contain elements of the two drives, hostility and love. Under certain circumstances the affectionate aspect of the investment of the emotion predominates but, if the love object disappoints or "hurts" the lover, the aggressive or hate aspect of the attachment may promptly rise to ascendancy.

Psychoanalytic experience has revealed the importance of eliciting information about the historical background of the patient-parent relationship, because of the fact that our attitudes are so dependent upon early experiences with our parents. Thus, throughout life one's reactions toward women are patterned after the relationship established toward the mother or mother substitute. One's adult attitude toward men and authority is largely determined by his early relationships with his father or father substitute.

Psychoanalytic study has contributed greatly to our understanding of behavior through its identification of the various methods of disposing of aggressions. The misdirection of the aggressive drive is the basic cause of all maladjustment. Early social experience within the family determines the method the individual uses in handling the aggressive drive, i.e., whether it is directed internally toward self-destructiveness or externally, and what devices are used for neutralizing or converting this energy.

---

[17] S. Freud, "Mourning and Melancholia," *Collected Papers*, IV, 152–170; "The Unconscious," *Collected Papers*, IV, 98–136.

This presentation of the fundamentals of psychoanalytic psychiatry would seem justified for two reasons. First, although these facts are widely known in psychiatric circles, their greatest importance is to medicine as a whole. Unfortunately, to date the average physician has not had even a working understanding of the unconscious. Second, a more adequate knowledge of ourselves should enable us to live richer and more satisfying lives. Consequently, it should be made readily available to the average man.

In presenting this brief review of psychoanalytic psychiatry, however, it would be gross neglect not to indicate that this interpretation of human behavior has contributed to realms other than those of psychiatry and medicine. Freud shed light on many of the problems of everyday life; [18] he made numerous applications to literature and art, [19] religion, [20] and social group behavior. [21] These were, however, more in the nature of by-products of his chief interest; they were somewhat speculative applications of the knowledge he had gained from clinical

---

[18] S. Freud, *Totem and Taboo* (New York: New Republic, Inc., 1927); *The Psychopathology of Everyday Life* (London: Fisher & Unwin, 1914).

[19] S. Freud, "The Moses of Michael Angelo," *Collected Papers*, IV, 257–287; *Leonardo da Vinci* (New York: Moffat, Yard & Co., 1916).

[20] S. Freud, *The Future of an Illusion* (New York: Liveright, 1928); *Moses and Monotheism* (London: Hogarth Press and the Institute of Psycho-Analysis, 1939).

[21] S. Freud, *Group Psychology and the Analysis of the Ego* (London: International Psychoanalytic Press, 1922).

findings. The primary result of his stimulus was that *all* of psychiatry as a branch of medicine has made *great* progress, well described by Galdston as follows:

Over and above all of the particulars of the great achievements of psychiatry, the greatest is this: that modern psychiatry has taught us to understand that the relationship of the individual to the group, insofar as it may require more of him than he is able to perform, can and does engender disease. . . . It has been demonstrated that man may become sick because his social relations are defective, because his social environment is noxious, or because of innate, hereditary, or acquired inability to deal adequately with his social relations—that is, with the reality he faces. . . . Lastly, medicine has gone beyond the "soil" into the realm of the psychosociological. This is by far the greatest achievement in medicine.[22]

---

[22] *Progress in Medicine* (New York: Alfred A. Knopf, 1940), p. 279.

Chapter 3

Psychiatry and
the Social Order

To FORMULATE the relationships between the actual and potential contributions of psychiatry and our present social order is a challenging task and a formidable one. In attempting to do so, one is handicapped by the limitations of his own experience and knowledge of psychiatry. Moreover, one person's awareness and knowledge of the numerous aspects of our social order is limited and probably biased, perhaps even prejudiced. Therefore, a discussion of these relationships becomes a matter of personal point of view. It is colored by one's optimism or pessimism, by one's confidence or lack of faith in psychiatry as well as in the topsy-turvy world of today.[1]

Daily perusal of the headlines of newspapers and occasional reading of magazines—which is as far as most of us go in informing ourselves about the present social order—leave us feeling distressed, concerned, and even anxious. We have made remarkable gains in our technological knowledge. Our advanced understanding of physical science, as represented by the atomic bomb, television,

---

[1] Many of the points in this lecture were presented to the American Psychiatric Association in May, 1947 (W. C. Menninger, "The Role of Psychiatry in the World Today," *Am. J. Psychiatry*, 104: 155–163, Sept., 1947). They were modified for presentation in the *Atlantic Monthly*, 181: 65–72 (Jan., 1948). Many are discussed in detail in a book by the author entitled *Psychiatry in a Troubled World* (New York: Macmillan Co., 1948).

and transportation, is so far beyond that of social science that our very existence is dangerously threatened. We have learned how to eliminate space and to annihilate people, but we have not discovered how to get along with each other.

We are still all too conscious of the cataclysmic effects of the World War on prices, taxes, shortages, and on national and international policies. Few of us can realize the true extent of the national indebtedness of America, Britain, and Canada because in prosecuting the war they spent nearly 500 billion dollars, such an astronomical figure that it has little meaning for most of us. Of this amount America paid out 157 million dollars a day for a period of over five years. Even so, the monetary cost was by all odds the least cost compared to that of the suffering, the distress, the destruction, and the death that occurred. Such a pathological outpouring of aggression and destructiveness might well be regarded as a world psychosis. The overt outlet of killing that the shooting war provided is again cut off in much of the world, but even an optimist cannot regard our present world status as a stage of convalescence.

The extent and seriousness of the postwar problems to be solved by individuals and by nations shroud our thinking like a heavy fog. We have trouble interpreting the experiences of the recent past in terms of a rapidly changing present. We are uneasy about where and how fast we are going and what is happening beyond our vision. The headlines tell us that millions of people are desperate for food and look to America to supply it. The economic stability of great nations is teetering, and that means insecurity in millions of families. International relations are filled with suspicion, tension, mistrust, and selfishness. We are becoming so allergic to vetoes and major disagreements in international councils, and the consequent lack of co-operation in meeting critical problems, that it is difficult to remain objective.

It may be that some of us have not entirely relinquished the anxiety built up during the years of 1941 to 1945. We are afraid; we see "fronts" being established along certain borders in the continents of Europe and Asia. We are confused when our actions are misinterpreted in other countries, and disturbed by what is to us unfairly conceived counter action. However, there is no excuse or substitute for bending our every effort toward achieving our greatest need, namely, to improve human relationships. An informed physician-statesman-soldier has recently told us, with authority, that so destructive have new weapons become that another major war could annihilate most of the human race.[2]

Whether or not we regard the world today as sick is a problem in the meaning of words. Certainly there is dramatic and conclusive evidence to indicate that too high a percentage of the world's population is terribly unhappy, and therefore unhealthy mentally. The situation of most of the world is somewhat reminiscent of our

---

[2] G. B. Chisholm, "On the March for Mental Health," *Survey Graphic*, 36: 509–511 (Oct., 1947).

psychiatric experience in the war. In civilian life the psychiatrist attempts to understand and treat people for their abnormal reactions to normal situations. In military life he had to understand and treat the normal reactions to highly abnormal situations. The condition of the world now places many people in a continuously abnormal situation to which they are reacting normally, even though by all previous standards their behavior is pathological. In such a turbulent world one might legitimately ask, what *is* a normal reaction?

The question also arises whether psychiatry has anything to offer toward a better understanding of social problems and their solution. The chief job of the psychiatrist has been, is, and always will be the treatment of those individuals whose maladjustment, in part at least, is the result of the sorry state of the social order, whose illnesses are reactions to the stresses in their environment. Psychiatrists, like all other doctors, have been concerned chiefly with individuals and, in fact, are regarded with a little suspicion if they invest much time and effort in community, national, or international affairs or politics. Their own preoccupation with more patients than they can care for properly, as well as the public attitude, has in some degree isolated them from participation in the study of social problems.

The experience of psychiatrists in the Army and Navy brought home to them and their associates, their superior officers, and their patients the decisive role that a stressful environment plays in mental illness. To many people, reduction of stress and increase in support by changes that can be made in the environment are as important in the maintenance of mental health as the making of changes in the personality. Psychiatry is proving to be a social science as well as a medical science.

The solution of our major social problems can be arrived at only through the pooling of the experience and knowledge of experts in many walks of life. Psychiatry, psychology, sociology, and anthropology, are all devoted to the study and understanding of how men think, feel, and behave. Psychiatry has accumulated an extensive body of knowledge about the anatomy and physiology of the personality. It has arrived at an explanation of man's aggressiveness toward his environment as well as toward himself. It has gathered information regarding the development of the personality and can shed light in some degree on much of the behavior of man as a social being. Psychiatry has contributed particularly to the effect of environment on the formation of the personality and the subsequent development of certain types of social behavior as expressions of internal psychological needs. The social sciences have acquired considerable knowledge on how man creates his environment and how he uses it to express, primarily, his individual needs and, secondarily, those of a social unit.

As a consequence of accumulating this knowledge about man and his behavior, it is reasonable to assume that psychiatry could and should make a contribution to the

understanding of some of the countless social problems
that surround us today.

THE INDIVIDUAL AND THE SOCIAL ORDER

The survey of the relationships between psychiatry
and the social order can be made best in terms of the individual, his relationships and activities. Most of the interest and practice of psychiatry in civilian life is
concerned entirely with the individual patient. By contrast, in the military service the psychiatrist, in order to
succeed in his job of maintaining man power, had to be
oriented to the role of the individual as a member of a
group. Therefore, in prescribing treatment for one person the health of all others in his unit became the primary
concern.

A detailed understanding of an individual personality
does not adequately explain the reactions of groups of
people. The whole is more than the sum of its component parts, and therefore the total reaction of a group of
persons is not merely the sum of the reaction of each of
its members. However, many clues to the understanding
of a social unit are found in an intensive study of the
individual. In this study psychiatry can take the lead.

Beginning with the individual, as psychiatry does, we
see that the average person unravels his life from day to
day, sometimes with plans, usually with hope, struggling
with his own limitations against the ever-changing external world. Each personality adjusts itself within the

limits of its capacity as it finds direct and indirect means of obtaining security and satisfaction. Each is confronted with minor and major emergencies and crises.

Most if not all of us are concerned chiefly with those persons, problems, and influences that bear most directly upon us. We are only momentarily bothered about the troubled world. Most of us in America read with equanimity the fact that millions of people in Europe are living on a thousand calories a day. Even the horror of war meant little to most persons unless their loved ones were involved in it by being in an area of danger. Our apparent complacency stems from our feeling of inability to ameliorate the widespread suffering or eradicate its causes. Quite understandably, therefore, most of us are vitally concerned only with the problems arising from our own everyday relationships—the hostility of an employer, economic pressure, problems in our love life, illness of the baby, our physical health, and so on.

The psychiatrist thinks of all these problems as sources of emotional stress, which place extra burdens on the personality in its daily functioning. Each personality is limited in its capacity to adjust itself, to withstand those stresses and continue to maintain equilibrium. This capacity varies widely in individuals because all of us are predisposed to poor handling of specific types of stresses as a result of our infancy and childhood experiences.

In understanding the individual's struggle, however, we must not assume that it is only the current immediate stresses that determine the reaction. Stresses can be cumulative, that is, the longer they continue the greater their force. Personal stresses combine forces with the stress of the social issues of the community in direct proportion to one's emotional maturity and intellectual capacity.

Sooner or later, the problems of the community, the nation, and the world become stresses for all of us. Only as we become personally aware of the fact that our neighbour's problems are our problems, that the solution of these is essential for our own survival, that the world is small—then and only then do the nonpersonal problems become personal threats. One does not seriously attempt to solve problems until they threaten him or his. Fortunately, an increasing number of citizens are aware that social issues are matters worthy of their greatest concern. From the psychiatrist's point of view they may and do become very real stresses for our more mature citizens, who pass these on in varying degree to the less mature. There is no question whatever that the immediate personal environmental stresses for many of us are augmented by the threats arising from the desperate needs of so many people in these troubled times.

One way in which the environmental stress can take its toll is illustrated by the discharge of over seven hundred thousand men from military service because of personality problems.[8] In many, these existed before the service began, but in the majority the problems were aggravated or created by the war experience. It is often said that

_____

[8] Figures from Medical Statistics Division, Surgeon General's Office (Army), 1946.

statistics can be made to tell almost any story, but even the most optimistic interpreter would have difficulty in discerning favorable aspects to our findings from the draft examination. By the war's end, nearly two million selectees had been rejected as unacceptable for military service because of personality problems. These men were not mentally ill but were considered to be poor risks to withstand unusually severe or markedly increased stress. Many of them were able to maintain their equilibrium as civilians and will never need to see a psychiatrist, but in varying degrees, their adjustment capacity was regarded as being limited or impaired. In other words, they were less healthy and effective than they should have been.

Various social problems—broken homes, unemployment, educational deficiencies, crowded housing—show up in the case histories of so many of these men that one cannot escape the conclusion that the emotional stress resulting from these factors played a part in producing the personality disability.

By various computations some fourteen million persons in the United States will sooner or later be incapacitated in some degree by mental illness.[4] This number of sick people will affect one out of every five families. Even these figures do not present the total picture of the nation's mental health problem. Just as we have minor

---

[4] K. Appel, *Our State Hospitals: What Can We Do To Improve Them?* (Chicago University Round Table Pamphlet, no. 496, Sept. 21, 1947).

physical disorders, we all have minor psychological disorders. While not serious, they are the cause of off-days, days we can't work, emotional blowups that upset other people. Transient distress all too easily and often grows into prolonged ineffectiveness and unhappiness.

The true meaning of the figures quoted is that a great number of people are subject to more stress than they can handle and receive too little support against it. We dare not play ostrich any longer to such an unpleasant and disconcerting fact. Only as we become informed about the condition is it possible to take constructive steps to prevent or remedy it.

What can the individual do as just one member of a social unit amid all the stresses that surround us? Obviously, the first step is to become informed about their sources, and the second is to take action toward reducing or removing them or strengthening people sufficiently to meet them.

Information about emotional stress involves education about mental health that would give a clear understanding of the factors essential to maintaining that health. This would entail an evaluation of the stresses and the supports that all of us experience in contacts with the family, friends, jobs, interests; also the recognition of good individual and group morale, and of the signs of breakdown of that morale. Mental health education would teach the individual how to be a part of the social group and how to participate constructively in social living. It would present knowledge about psychological maturity, which is really the result of successful adjustment to earlier development and knowledge of its goal. The mature person finds his chief satisfaction and gratification in life in sharing, giving, creating, loving. Maturity requires one to give up and to outgrow selfishness, narrowmindedness, prejudice, hypocrisy. It implies awareness that love is a far more powerful motivating force than is hate and that the main purpose of our individual lives and our collective efforts must be to direct our powerful aggressive and destructive instincts into constructive outlets.

Social action must rest on the basis of knowledge of ourselves and of social forces. The first step then is to educate ourselves. Such education must be followed, however, by the utilization and the application of such knowledge not only to our personal lives but to our families and the groups of which we are a part, by exercising discrimination in the choice of our leaders, by combining our influence with that of like-minded individuals in order to produce sufficient social pressure to accomplish our aims. A glance at our social order leaves little doubt of the fact that, if we as individuals wish to enjoy mental health, many drastic reforms are necessary in almost every area of living. These can only be produced, in our democratic culture, through the united efforts of enlightened, determined, intellectually and emotionally mature individuals.

THE FAMILY

The chief supports or hindrances for the individual in his struggle to adjust himself are found in the family. Whether he develops emotional maturity depends very largely upon his home and his parents. As adults we are the result of our childhood and adolescent experiences. The psychiatrist is convinced that emotional maturity can be reached only through a childhood experience in a situation that provides affection, good example, and security. The number of precariously adjusted personalities, indicated by the rejection and discharge figures given above, show that too many homes have not provided such conditions. Perhaps the current trend of change in our family structure, at least in many families, prevents the home from satisfying the basic emotional needs of children.

Family relationships and the responsibilities of its members are changing. Various statistics can be marshaled as evidence of this. In 1945 there was one divorce for every two new marriages in urban areas and one for every three new marriages in the country at large. In figures, the divorces increased from approximately two hundred fifty thousand in 1937 to over five hundred thousand in 1945.[5] Before the war, approximately eleven million women worked outside the home (two and one-

---

[5] B. L. Jenkinson, "Marriage and Divorce in the United States: 1937–1945," *Vital Statistics, Bureau of Census, Special Report,* vol. 23, no. 9, Sept. 10, 1946.

half million more wanted or needed work). In July, 1947, there were over eighteen million women at work away from home, seven million of whom were married.[6] At present 47.1 per cent of our families have no children under nineteen years of age and an additional 21.6 per cent have only one child.[7] Various surveys have indicated that college-graduated women are producing far fewer than the number of children required to take their places. Similarly, college-graduated men have fewer offspring than the number required to replace them though the difference is less than in the case of women.[8]

Though there are no figures to "prove" it, in looking about us we can feel sure there is less shared activity and a weaker sense of family loyalty than in the days of restricted social contacts and bigger, more stable homesteads. Many factors are at work in changing the family. Communications and transportation have increased the tempo of its life. Economic pressure and striving for psychological satisfaction have altered the traditional pattern of man as wage earner and woman as homemaker. The machine age has very radically changed the routine of living of wives and mothers who remain at home as housewives. There is widespread current discussion in our magazines of the psychological problems that this

[6] Quoted from U.S. Department of Labor in the *New York Times,* Sept. 14, 1947.

[7] *A Program for National Security* (Washington, D.C.: U.S. Govt. Print. Office, 1947), p. 170.

[8] Figures available from the Population Reference Bureau, Washington, July, 1947.

change presents to the housewife and her household.[9]

Psychiatrists uniformly agree that the great majority of psychological cripples receive the injuries that predispose them to their crippled state in childhood, very often even in infancy. Only the parents can furnish the environment adequate in affection and security that will guarantee mental health for their children in later life. Consequently, one of the most tangible and specific actions that any of us who are parents or who expect to become parents or who are teaching potential parents can do is to gain the necessary information about how to provide children with an opportunity to become emotionally mature. This is critically imperative in a world that so sorely needs psychologically mature citizens.

THE COMMUNITY

Another major support, always potential and in many places actual, is the community. Historically, communities arose because of the mutual need for support and defense of the individuals composing them. Again, if we are honest and look about us, we see too many indications of community mismanagement, selfishness, graft. One of the widespread social maladjustments is the phenomenon of isolationism whereby we assume that our family can

---

[9] Illustrative articles are: Della D. Cyrus, "What's Wrong with the Family?" *Atlantic Monthly*, 178: 67–73 (Nov., 1946); Della D. Cyrus, "Why Mothers Fail," *Atlantic Monthly*, 179: 57–60 (March, 1947); "It's up to the Women: A Symposium," *Atlantic Monthly*, 179: 39–46 (June, 1947); Sidonie M. Gruenberg, "The Modern Mother's Dilemma," *Child Study*, 24: 100–103 (Summer-Fall, 1947).

get along regardless of the failure of other families to do so, or that our community can function regardless of other communities, or that our nation can live in spite of the state of affairs in other nations.

Other evidences of our community maladjustment may be mentioned briefly. One is the widespread prejudice and discrimination against persons because of race, color, or religion. Bigoted intolerance, the thesis of "white supremacy," anti-Semitic prejudice, discriminatory practices, hostile attitudes toward Catholicism and Protestantism are all present in varying degrees in every section of the country.[10] Unfortunately they are present in every part of the world. They must be regarded as another evidence of emotional immaturity—sometimes of fear, often as a collective device by which we project the devil within ourselves onto others. No one can be unaware in our present community life of the emotional cost to everyone concerned of labor-management disputes and misunderstandings. Another acute problem of our communities that is vital to mental health is the housing situation, particularly as it affects our large number of veterans and war workers. If we have reached emotional maturity ourselves, we cannot regard the many social problems of our community with complacency when they so vitally affect our mental health, happiness, and effectiveness, whether or not we recognize specific personal disadvantage.

---

[10] See *Fortune* magazine survey of October, 1947, for current picture of racial and religious intolerance.

It is the responsibility of each of us, as individuals who make up the integral parts of our communities and nation and world, to take considered action toward corrective measures in all these matters. Only as the community provides educational opportunities for our children, public utilities, protection of our health, opportunities for social outlets, and many other things can it serve as a support. But only if we as citizens see that these are provided can the community make them available.

The corollary to providing community facilities is to be sure that those who are in trouble know about these facilities and take advantage of them. A recent sociological study was very revealing in its discovery that families in trouble either did not know what community services could help them or avoided their use because of previous unsatisfactory experience with them.[11]

The way man feels and behaves depends in considerable degree upon the emotional stresses and the supports in the environment in which he lives. If the stresses are great and the community cannot provide support, a man who has a choice of where he will live chooses another community or nation. Much more significant, however, are the more common situations in which a man can have no choice. He must remain where he is, and as a result his fears, frustrations, and needs pile up emotional burdens. These stresses may be the influential pressures that lead to his consideration and even acceptance of ways to

---

[11] E. L. Koos, *Families in Trouble* (New York: King's Crown Press, 1946).

escape: neurosis, suicide, psychosis, and belief in various ideologies. These psychological forces, inseparably linked with mental health, are what make certain nations look East or West. They are the same neurotic and irrational forces that lead us into war.[12] But *we* make our environment, and must assume responsibility for it. There are many areas where we have failed and are failing. In many others we are only beginning to pool our knowledge and experience to bring about improvement.

It is pertinent to review the working relationships of psychiatry and certain activities within our social order, namely, education, industry, criminology, penology, and public health.

PSYCHIATRY AND EDUCATION

From the psychiatrist's point of view, much of the basic knowledge of the personality could not only be of great benefit to the pedagogue but, were it applied, might very radically influence the methods used and the courses given throughout our educational system. This assumption is predicated on three facts: first, that the psychiatrist regards the development of personality very largely as an educational procedure; second, that the teacher can aid or hinder the child in his adjustment; third, that counseling of students has become a necessity and not merely a frill.

[12] G. B. Chisholm, "The Reestablishment of Peacetime Society," *Psychiatry*, 9: 3–11 (Feb., 1946).

The parents undoubtedly are the most important among the child's educators, but the school teacher stands very close in second place. The psychiatrist has unlimited evidence that the individual has to learn through experience and trial and error the basic living patterns that make our lives successful or unsuccessful. For example, the individual has to learn how to love, a fact that is very often entirely ignored. He has to learn to tolerate frustrations, to make readjustments and compromises, to live and co-operate with people, to find satisfactions in assigned, even though unpleasant, tasks. Our high rate of neuroticism indicates too clearly how poorly many of these lessons were learned and therefore how poorly they were taught. One's early years are an education in how to live. Most of these lessons are barely started when the child begins his formal academic education.

The second evidence of the potential value of a psychiatric orientation for teachers is gleaned from the psychiatrist's daily practice with children and young adults. Again and again the patient's life history reveals not only that opportunities were missed by the teacher in aiding the individual in his adjustment, but also that in many instances the maladjustment reached a climax because of experiences in his formal education. The converse of this was true when the right help was available from the teacher at the right time. Most teachers do not have information about personality development and adjustment. Without this knowledge they fail to recognize the evidence of maladjustment, which can completely foil their efforts to ladle out information and teach skills.

Ask a teacher in an American public school why a particular child cries in class, why another seems fearful or rebellious, why still another fails in spite of his "smartness." One will probably receive a sincere but superficial answer to the effect that "She is just a peculiar child," "She doesn't apply herself," "He is spoiled," or "He is lazy." This simply means that the teacher does not really know that she does not know why.[13]

This is not an attempt to depreciate our teachers; rather, it is a plea for attention to an unfortunate fact. Teacher-training programs have been inadequate in this regard. This is due partly to a scarcity of qualified instructors, as well as of good texts, in this area, and partly to the fairly recent realization that educational psychology courses are no substitute for instruction in child development, personality structure, and personality adjustment. Teachers have been so overloaded with pupils that there has been little or no time to give to the problems of individual children. Moreover, the indifference of the American public allows such low salary schedules to remain in force that we are losing many of our best teachers. It is reported that we have lost 350,000 since 1939, a third of the total number of school teachers in America.

[13] K. A. Menninger, *The Human Mind* (3d ed., New York: Alfred A. Knopf, 1945), pp. 421–433.

PSYCHIATRY AND THE SOCIAL ORDER

The third point of evidence of the potential value of psychiatric knowledge to the teacher has been gained from the experience psychiatry has had in educational institutions. To my knowledge, the first college course in mental hygiene was offered by my brother at Washburn University in 1919. Undoubtedly, counseling of varying types had been offered in some colleges and universities before that time. In the intervening twenty-eight years preventive psychiatry has been presented as mental hygiene either in the form of courses or in counseling services in a few of our high schools and in some of our colleges and universities.

It is the generally accepted opinion among school and college psychiatrists that a fair proportion of students need mental hygiene counseling; a high percentage could profit from it. Very few of their problems are solved in the courses they take. The mortality in the freshman class of every university is mute evidence of our failure to provide assistance with the adjustment of too many potential college students.

Whatever the conception of educators about the ideal purposes of higher education, most college courses are primarily and often solely a vehicle for passing out vast quantities of factual information. Professors and instructors are more often selected for their erudition and publications than for their ability to present more or less dull subject matter in such a way as to stimulate students to think about it. Nor is their interest in furthering healthy adjustment of students a criterion for their selection. As

David Levy pointed out, one may find brilliant students whose personalities are immature, eccentric, thwarted, and incapable of maintaining social relations. "There will be little disagreement among psychiatrists who deal with college students, or with faculty for that matter, as to the meager values of the courses taken at college as an aid to social adjustment." [14]

Any and all education should teach a man how to live and to make a living. This is obviously a very complicated process and should determine the selection of subject matter, methods of presentation, and teaching personalities in any school. We cannot provide a liberating education merely through a long intellectual development that leaves the problems of personal and social adjustment to fraternity experience, campus activities, and college atmosphere. If the aim of an education is to develop the whole man, we must introduce courses and a total program that will promote emotional and social adjustment as well as provide intellectual opportunity.

Fortunately, the failure of our formal education to produce mature individuals is becoming more widely recognized. Not only have psychiatrists recognized this to be true, but even industry is beginning to express itself about the immature personalities turned out of our schools. Recently, or comparatively so, on the recommendation of New York City employers, personality courses were introduced into twenty-seven vocational

---

[14] D. Levy, *New Fields of Psychiatry* (New York: W. W. Norton & Co., 1946), p. 70.

high schools. This was done on the ground that employees lose their jobs because of personal immaturity and not lack of job skill.[15]

A few of our educators are pioneering in their thinking in this area in the hope that personality guidance will change the program of producing "vocational morons and academic geniuses" [16] to one of promoting a higher degree of vocational maturity. Howard Mumford Jones has expressed himself to the effect that "a wider understanding of the psychology of personal relationships seems to me a more desperate need in our education than polite courses in literature, philosophy and the fine arts." [17] The trend in the direction of the utilization of psychiatry is indicated by the increasing number of teacher's colleges that include courses in personality study. In the last ten years several excellent texts prepared specifically for the use of teachers have dealt with mental hygiene and personality adjustments.

More and more colleges and universities offer mental hygiene courses and counseling services. Just prior to the third national conference on health in colleges this last year, Doctor C. E. Shepard [18] made a survey of a thousand colleges and universities. Three hundred question-

---

[15] G. F. Pigott, Jr., Assistant Superintendent of Schools, New York City; quoted in Science Research Associates, *Guidance News Letter* (Chicago), Sept., 1947.

[16] S. A. Hamrin, of Northwestern University; quoted in *ibid.*

[17] H. M. Jones, *Education and World Tragedy* (Cambridge, Mass.: Harvard University Press, 1946), p. 106.

[18] Personal communication, Sept. 12, 1947.

naires were returned with fairly complete information. Among the items on them were several concerning mental hygiene. A hundred and fifty-two colleges stated that "medical counselling in mental hygiene" is available to students; one hundred forty-five colleges stated that psychiatric consultation is available through the student health service; ninety colleges stated that courses in mental hygiene are offered for college credit. On seventy-nine returns giving information on this point, the course is required in thirteen instances and elective in sixty-six. These figures, however, give us no evaluation of the type and quality of mental hygiene provided either in the courses or in counseling, nor of the number of instances in which this service is given by a psychiatrist. Nevertheless, they do indicate an increasing trend toward the provision of this service and an increasingly closer relationship between psychiatry and education.

PSYCHIATRY AND INDUSTRY

Industry is another area in which there have been only a few direct contacts and relationships with psychiatry. Elmer Ernest Southard pioneered in this direction when he became interested in the reasons why men were discharged from their jobs. He found, and his findings have been substantiated by others, that in the great majority of instances failure on the job was due to personality difficulties and not to deficiency in job skills.[19] Later,

---

[19] E. E. Southard, "The Movement for a Mental Hygiene of Industry," *Mental Hyg.*, 4: 43–64 (Jan., 1920).

V. V. Anderson established a psychiatric clinic in a large New York department store.[20] Since that time there have been many contacts between psychiatry and industry, though surprisingly few of the established programs are carried on by a full-time psychiatrist. At the present time there are probably not more than six or eight psychiatrists who devote their efforts full time to industrial or business organizations although there are many who act as consultants to various concerns.

Industrial psychiatry, as we have learned to know it, has many elements in common with military psychiatry. The psychiatrist himself must become indoctrinated with the purpose of the organization with which he is associated. He must learn its methods and its problems and become closely identified with it. His aim must be to accomplish the mission of the particular industry, and he must accept the priority of importance of the group rather than of any individual in the group, just as he does in the Army. Much of his work is of a preventive nature and is applied in personnel selection, in placement, and in adjustment to the job. He must by necessity run an emotional "first-aid station."

One special feature in some types of industry has a particular psychiatric significance, namely, accidents.[21]

---

[20] V. V. Anderson, *Psychiatry and Industry* (New York: Harper & Bros., 1929).

[21] Numerous medical articles have appeared on the subject of accident proneness. See L. D. Bristol, "Medical Aspects of Accident Control," *J.A.M.A.*, 107: 653–655 (Aug. 29, 1936); F. Dunbar, "Medical Aspects of Accidents," *War Medicine*, 4: 161–185 (Aug., 1943);

We have learned to recognize that in certain personalities there is an unconscious need for punishment, which is expressed by a proneness to accidents. There is statistical evidence to indicate that a very high percentage of accidents occurs in a very small percentage of employees. This ratio applies in all types of mechanical occupations from machine work to truck driving. Certain individuals have a tendency to become sick frequently, and over the period of a year we find a high percentage of absences due to sickness occurring in a small percentage of the employees. Insofar as these can be detected, such individuals often can be helped. When such help is not possible, the industrial concern can effect material savings by replacing them with other less sick-prone employees. An increasing number of industrial and business concerns are now providing a so-called "counseling" service, a progressive and economic step. Many of these are excellent, though their success depends upon the training and capability of the counselors. On this point, however, the psychiatrist feels impelled to sound a note of warning. Insofar as counselors are responsible only for giving advice about job placement and immediate problems in the environment, all may be well. Even then, however, it is essential that such counselors have specific training. Unfortunately, too often the problems presented are a matter of health, occasionally physical health but very often mental health. In such instances there is

A. H. Rawson, "Accident Proneness," *Psychosomatic Med.*, 6: 88–94 (Jan., 1944).

no question that if treatment is to be given, it should be given by a physician. In the majority of instances, because of the frequency of emotional problems, this physician is best equipped if he has a psychiatric orientation. Ideally, he can serve best if he has had psychiatric training.

CRIMINOLOGY

In the role of student and interpreter of bizarre human behavior, the psychiatrist has had a deep interest in all types of misbehavior whether classified in legal terms as crime, misdemeanor, or delinquency, or in medical language as neurotic or psychopathic or psychotic behavior. The lawyer or judge is interested in equality, justice, responsibility, punishment. The psychiatrist is interested in motivation, psychopathology, treatment. For the most part, psychopathology is not taught in law schools, and psychiatric legal problems are not taught in medical schools.

Consequently, the schools of thought in law and in medicine, as represented by psychiatrists, are so far apart that there still prevails more misunderstanding than understanding. The situation was well summarized in a statement made by Judge Roscoe Pound, who, at the time, was Dean of the Harvard Law School:

Despite all that the criminologists have done in the last generation, the criminal law is still framed chiefly in terms of punishing the vicious will. Despite all that criminologists and physicians have shown as to the necessity of special institutions with expert management for many classes of delinquents, the legal theory of ideal equality before the law leads the criminal law, whenever it is in the hands of lawyers, to consign all to a common prison.

Despite all that psychiatry and psychology have achieved, the lawyer can draw only a plain straight line between an artificial legal conception of insanity and a no less artificial legal conception of normal responsibility.

Where anything has been accomplished in the way of individualization of penal treatment, in almost every case it has had to be done through administrative boards and commissions, acting on principles radically different from those of the criminal courts, and with courts and bar largely out of sympathy with them.[22]

Psychiatry has had a limited contact with our judicial system in three ways: the commitment of mental cases to hospitals, the presence of psychiatrists as experts in criminal cases, and the utilization of psychiatrists and their associates as neutral assistants to the court to study offenders and delinquents.

Psychiatry has had an unfortunate relationship to our legal processes because of the requirement of legal commitment of patients to state hospitals. Historically, in early statutes a commitment was necessary only for the dangerously insane. Later it became the procedure to commit all patients. The legal process has tended to stigmatize the mentally ill person as a criminal. "The men-

---

[22] Quoted from *The Human Mind,* by K. A. Menninger, pp. 443–444.

tally ill person may be arrested by a sheriff with a warrant, charged with insanity by a judge, retained in a jail pending a hearing, tried in an open court before a jury, remanded to jail pending a vacancy in a mental hospital and finally transported to a hospital by a sheriff." [23]

Many of our states are still medieval in not recognizing mental illness as a medical problem and handling it entirely as such. For instance, in twenty-one states a trial by jury is still an essential feature of the commitment law, and it is mandatory in two—Texas and Mississippi.[24] Gradually, however, a change is taking place. Now all but six states have a procedure that permits a patient to go to a state hospital voluntarily if he, his family, or his physician feel this is necessary. But the fact remains that there are still six states in which this process is not permitted. In a surprisingly large number of our states the procedure of entrance into a state hospital is archaic and leads inevitably to stigmatization of the patient, adding a great injury to the individual's self-pride.

Commitment to a state hospital is tantamount to legal incompetence in many states. In many instances the patient is made a public spectacle, and a public record is made of his illness. There is no reason why a jury should be expected to know any more about mental illness than

---

[23] F. N. Flaschner, "Analysis of Legal and Medical Considerations in Commitment of the Mentally Ill," *Yale Law Journal*, 56: 1178–1209 (Aug., 1947).

[24] See *Circular Letter No. 50*, Sept. 30, 1947, Group for the Advancement of Psychiatry, Report of Committee on Forensic Psychiatry, Chairman, Dr. Manfred Guttmacher.

it does about physical illness. Its judgment should not be the criterion for a diagnosis of mental illness any more than for appendicitis.

It is to be hoped that before long the legal profession need not be involved in this totally medical problem. We must look forward and work for the time when certification of the existence of an illness is adequate evidence for hospitalization without the necessity for legal steps for commitment or the deprivation of legal rights. Such stigmatization has led people to fear the state hospital rather than to regard it as a potential source of help.

The second area of contact, namely, where psychiatrists serve as experts in special cases, has had a decidedly unfavorable effect upon psychiatry in the eyes of both the court and the public. This unfortunate state of affairs has been brought about because of the rigidity of our legal system, which permits both the prosecution and the defense to employ their own specialists to testify from their points of view.

There have been and always will be psychological problems of offenders that can justifiably be subject to conflicting viewpoints if studied by several psychiatrists. Our fund of knowledge is still too meager and our points of view too divergent to make it possible, or perhaps even advisable, for several psychiatrists to agree entirely on the nature of the problem of each patient. This healthy disagreement occurs regularly in psychiatric practice and results in progress. Therefore it is not surprising that differences of opinion might occur among sincere and reliable experts with regard to an offender. But to an uninformed public such differences bring discredit to psychiatry.

The medicolegal committee of the American Psychiatric Association has gone on record repeatedly [25] to urge that when psychiatric opinion is needed the court should appoint a neutral commission as an aid to the court and forbid the testimony of individuals employed by one or the other side. Unfortunately little progress has been made in this direction.

The third area in which psychiatrists have had contact with our legal system has been in the courts where they were appointed as either part-time or full-time advisors. The first psychiatric clinic in connection with a court was established in Chicago in 1914. Since then many similar psychiatric services have developed in connection with both adult and juvenile courts. The actual number of courts having such service is unknown. At least nine adult criminal courts have psychiatric services regularly available, and perhaps twenty juvenile courts have organized psychiatric services. Many others in both categories make use of occasional psychiatric consultations.

By this plan, the court requests a psychiatric study and evaluation of the offender before he is tried. The information is then available to the court as an aid in deciding

---

[25] Between the years of 1924 and 1929, Dr. Karl A. Menninger, was chairman of the medicolegal committee of the American Psychiatric Association. During those years, this committee had several meetings with a committee from the American Bar Association. Their efforts are reported in *The Human Mind*, pp. 451–456.

the disposition of the offender. In almost no instances, however, does psychiatry function further than this point, and therefore it is limited to a diagnostic study, with such recommendations as it can make to the court. The great need is for carrying out a treatment program once it has been decided upon.

It is on this point of treatment, however, that the thinking of the legal profession diverges sharply from the point of view of psychiatrists. The major part of our criminal law is still based upon imposing a fitting punishment for a given crime without consideration of the motives, circumstances, or even the most effective disposition of the offender. From the psychiatrist's point of view, misbehavior of any type merits scientific study of its cause and of the most effective disposition of the person. Never should the criminal, any more than any other maladjusted person, be considered in terms of needing punishment. Often a serious effort could be made to change the personality. In other cases the aim might be to rehabilitate the offender to a sufficiently social and productive status in society. In still other instances, indefinite custody is essential for the protection of the individual and of society.

Psychiatrists would hold strongly to the belief that an indeterminate sentence is the only type that is consistent with our present scientific knowledge of human behavior. On the same basis, the judge's responsibility should be to determine the guilt of the offender and a panel of social scientists could best determine the program of rehabilitation and the eventual disposition. This whole problem of social misbehavior and our individual concern with it is of far more than theoretical importance. The number of crimes in 1946 exceeded any previous year with a total of 1,685,000 during the year, an increase over 1945 of 119,633.[26] In 1945 123,000 offenders passed through 374 juvenile courts. It is estimated that there are approximately 270,000 prisoners in our penitentiaries, jails, reformatories, and work houses.[27]

The cost of crime, which includes the care of the prisoners as well as maintaining our elaborate police systems, has been variously estimated to be between ten and eighteen billion dollars a year. Adult criminal justice is estimated to cost two hundred and fifty million dollars a year.[28]

Obviously many reforms must take place to reduce the staggering loss of man power and money. It would help greatly if our legal system could be so changed as to take into account our knowledge of the human personality. Progressive lawyers and psychiatrists hope for and are working for these changes. They never will come about, however, until public apathy and indifference about delinquency and crime change to enlightenment and social pressure for such reform.

---

[26] News release, Department of Justice, Federal Bureau of Investigation, March 5, 1947.

[27] Personal communication from J. V. Bennett, Director of Bureau of Federal Prisons, dated March 20, 1947.

[28] A. Morris, *Criminology* (New York: Longmans, Green & Co., 1938), p. 20.

PENOLOGY

Psychiatry has played a small but definite role in the penal institutions of our country. Unfortunately, this has been minimal. At the present time many posts are open for which no psychiatrists are available. It is roughly estimated that in 1940 there were approximately fifty full-time and part-time psychiatrists in penal work. All of our federal penitentiaries and detention homes are authorized to have a full-time psychiatrist, but in several instances these jobs are not filled. The opportunity for the psychiatrist to carry on a satisfying program has, however, in many if not in most penal institutions, been very limited. The impression gained from several psychiatrists in this field is that they are not particularly welcomed because their point of view differs so sharply from the customary atmosphere prevailing in prison.

For emotional reasons the public believes that the offender should be punished. For many years this has been the principle on which penal institutions have operated although, somehow or other, the prisoners are supposed to come out better for having been punished. There is no question that punishment does not in any way deter the average prisoner from continuing his anti-social behavior. On the other hand, experience in reformatories and prisons has shown that, in the majority of instances, the personality is more hardened in its anti-social ways because of the prison experience. In other words, rather than rehabilitating men, we are confirming them in their groove of antisocial behavior.

Along with the state hospitals, our jails, reformatories, and penitentiaries are a disgrace to our social order. They are a no-man's land to the average citizen. Many if not most of them continue one or more odious practices such as graft for the immediate operator, kangaroo courts, rock piles, and chain gangs. It may be news but it is not surprising that, as a result of inspection, the United States Bureau of Prisons condemned four-fifths of the jails as unfit for use by the Bureau.[29] All these medieval penal methods are strongly disapproved by our leading penologists and such organizations as the American Prison Association, but public indifference permits their continuance.

Psychiatry is interested because it regards social misbehavior as a symptom of a distorted personality, which in many instances can be helped. We do not consider that many offenders in our prisons are mentally sick, but that all are socially and therefore personally maladjusted. As long as the public demands punishment and incarceration, there is little hope that any scientific approach that is interested in treatment and appropriate disposition of each individual can make much headway. So long as functioning in this area of our social order is controlled

---

[29] *The Manual of Suggested Standards for a State Correctional System*, prepared by the American Prison Association, Committee on the Model State Plan, Oct., 1946, p. 82.

by emotions rather than by intelligence, the opportunity to apply the scientific principles of psychiatry is slim.

PUBLIC HEALTH

Psychiatry has made only a beginning in the realm of public health. Medicine, with its increased knowledge of prevention of illness and through the epidemiological approach and sanitation, has made phenomenal progress in safeguarding physical health. This function is almost entirely carried out by public health organizations.

In contrast to this progress, the prevention of mental ill health is not included in programs of the public health departments in many of our state governments. This remains true in spite of the fact that more deaths occur from one symptom of mental illness, namely, suicide, than from the five most common communicable diseases.

The backward state of affairs of mental hygiene in public health programs is undoubtedly due to the slow evolution of psychiatry. It is only within the last twenty-five years that we have acquired helpful knowledge of value in the prevention of mental ill health. Consequently, we have been greatly handicapped in developing a public health preventive program in psychiatry.

At the present time seven of our states (Connecticut, Florida, Kansas, Maine, Mississippi, Wisconsin, and Washington) have a psychiatrist as a member of their public health divisions. A few states have a mental hygiene unit that is separate from the state board of health, and in some other states a psychiatrist is in the Department of Welfare. In the majority of states the psychiatric program is limited to the supervision of the state hospitals. In a few of the more progressive states a program for the development of mental hygiene clinics has and is being developed. In only one or two is there any sort of program for the prevention of mental illness.

Within the last year the recognition of the importance of, and the opportunity for, psychiatry by the United States Public Health Service has given impetus to its greater use. After the initiation of action by the leaders in this service, Congress passed the National Mental Health Act in 1946. Through this legislation a considerable amount of money will be appropriated to promote the training of psychiatrists and workers in related fields. Federal grants will be made to develop and support psychiatric research. The most significant feature of the act for the public health program is permission to make grants-in-aid to states for the development of psychiatric facilities and programs within those states. When this act was passed, it was learned that many states did not even have an authorized state official with whom the United States Public Health Service could officially communicate about mental health, a significant indication of the backwardness of psychiatric programs in the state public health departments.

It is reasonable to assume that with our increased knowledge of preventive psychiatry we may look forward eventually to definite programs under state auspices for the prevention of mental ill health. Such programs will certainly include surveys of the extent of maladjustment and mental ill health, not only as indicated by the number of psychiatric patients but by the incidence of delinquency and crime, the divorce rate, and certain industrial problems. It is more than likely that special attention will be given to the development of facilities that could promote mental health programs in schools, churches, and clubs. The provision of vocational and recreational facilities would be essential. Most important will be a program of public education in mental hygiene.

Within all these areas of our social order—education, industry, criminology, penology, and public health—psychiatry has made some definite, even though as yet very inadequate, contacts. On the other hand, in every instance more progress has been made in the last ten years than in the previous century. We sorely lack knowledge tested by experience in these fields. In all of them there is an acute shortage of psychiatrically trained personnel even for the jobs now available. These developments serve to illustrate, however, one of the conspicuous trends of psychiatry at the present time, namely, an increased interest in and concern with the problems of our social order.

Psychiatrists do not mean to appear pretentious in their claims about what they may or may not be able to do toward a solution of various social issues. Such claims as are made, for the most part are based on very solid experience. Some of this was the varied experience of psychiatrists in the formation of the Army and its maintenance during the prosecution of the war. Psychiatrists carried on their customary but very extensive job of diagnosing and treating psychiatric patients. In addition, they entered the fields of selection, the placement of soldiers in jobs, the maintenance of morale, consideration of personnel policies, furnishing advice and counsel in training methods, and providing examinations and recommendations in cases of misbehavior. Psychiatry was called upon to step far beyond its customary role in civilian life to contribute to the total mission of the Army.

In so doing, psychiatrists learned many lessons. Among the most important of these was the fact that certain social factors were conducive to the maintenance, or contributed to the impairment, of mental health. Many of these factors are present also in civilian life situations and operate similarly. Because of their proven significance and their potential value as applied to the solution of civilian problems, three lessons are worthy of mention in connection with the role of psychiatry in the social order.

LEADERSHIP

Without doubt the one most important factor in the maintenance of mental health and the production of mental ill health in the Army was leadership. The chief conclusion of our observations was that where we had good leadership, we had a comparatively low psychiatric casualty rate; where we had poor leadership, the rate was high. There were many facets to this problem. It was repeatedly observed that men, who under individual scrutiny of the psychiatrist were classified as neurotic or somewhat unstable, carried on indefinitely under good leadership despite great external environmental stress. Conversely, men of excellent background, stamina, and personal integrity were seen to go to pieces under poor leadership.

There were too few opportunities to determine in any great detail the particular qualities that characterized a good leader. Some general qualities, however, were manifest consistently in the superior leader. Perhaps first and foremost was his consideration for the individuals for whom he was responsible, evidenced in such a way that they were aware of his confidence, trust, and personal interest in them. The good leader became the good father symbolically and as such assumed full responsibility of guaranteeing his men a fair chance, their share of provisions and comfort, and their protection insofar as it could be provided.

This record of the importance of leadership can be torn from the book of army experience and applied directly in the home to the parent, in the school to the teacher, in the community to its leaders, in the state and the government to our leaders there. Any leader, no matter who his followers may be, who by his behavior acquires the full confidence of his followers and by this confidence wins their unswerving loyalty, devotion, and willingness, furthers inestimably the maintenance of mental health. On the other hand, that leader who fails to lead, who fails to win the confidence of his followers, producing instead uncertainty and insecurity, is an influence toward poor mental health. These principles apply equally to the father and mother, the teacher and employer, the mayor and commissioner, the senator and congressman.

MOTIVATION

A second major influence for or against mental health in our Army was the degree of conscious motivation toward his job that could be created in the soldier. It was the difficult assignment of the Army to take millions of young men and women from civilian life and to try to convince them that the difficult and unpleasant job of fighting the war, with all of its inherent stresses and dangers, was a necessary thing to be done. One could hardly separate motivation from the influence of leadership.

In those instances where, through leadership and through a program of information and education, we could help a soldier to develop a conviction as to the importance of his job, we had minimal concern about his mental health. Where we found groups of men with strong positive motivation, we found low psychiatric casualty rates. On the contrary, when we found individuals or groups who felt that their jobs were unimportant, who because of disillusionment were "browned off," who because of mismanagement were disgruntled and disgusted, we always found a much higher psychiatric casualty rate.

This lesson has its direct applications to civilian life in every field of activity. It begins in the home situation where the parents have the responsibility for motivating the child toward assuming responsibility, toward doing his share of the tasks, toward accepting frustrations and the delay of pleasures as a part of the growing-up process. The educator has the opportunity to provide the motivation for the student to learn, and this the successful teacher recognizes as a necessity. The Army found it essential to develop an extensive education and information program to let the soldiers know how to do their job, but even more important was to let them know the reasons for and the relationships in their job. Groups of any size—clubs, organizations, municipalities, states, and nations—might profitably develop a similar system as an aid to motivating the members of their groups.

IDENTIFICATION

Motivation is closely related to and inseparable from the necessity of developing a social consciousness for accomplishing a mission. In the Army we often spoke of this as identification with the unit, that is, the individual became so closely linked with other members of his group that he was inseparable from them. His ideas, feelings, and attitudes were those of the group. He accepted the group opinion and was molded by it. He became so at one with it that the group consciousness, its mission, and its purpose were his personal motivating forces. What the group wanted to do, he wanted to do because he was such an integral part of it. This led to a group cohesiveness, pride, and unity of purpose.

Where units developed this social consciousness, we could always be sure that the mental casualties would be lower. When a man closely identified himself with his unit, he easily gave up his own personal interests and his highly individualized identity. In such instances, not only did the group more effectively accomplish its mission, but the individual members were more satisfied with their lot. The members of such a unit were likely to be far more healthy mentally than those who were so unfortunate as to be in outfits where such identification could not or did not take place.

This third lesson too has its applications to civilian life. If ever we are to make serious and extensive reforms in our social order, if we are to accomplish the solution of many of the problems outlined in this discussion, it will only be because groups of us can develop a social consciousness that eclipses our individual wishes. If we as individuals could become sufficiently mature emotionally and intellectually, if we could choose our leadership wisely, if we could educate ourselves to the problems at hand and identify ourselves sufficiently closely with the group to forego our individualism—if we could do all of this, we could eradicate even the greatest of our social problems. At the same time we could eliminate a very large percentage of our mental ill health.

Such a state would surely be Utopia. No psychiatrist is such a dreamer that he believes this is possible. Nevertheless, his job with his individual patients or in discussing the social problems of our troubled world is to help in facing reality as it exists in the problems of day-by-day life. His potential contribution, however, is to point out not only the psychopathology of everyday life, but also some of the factors that cause it and some of the factors that might tend to correct it. This has been my attempt in the presentation of the relationship of psychiatry to the problems of our social order.

Index

Abraham, Karl, 58 n., 61 n.
Accident proneness, 113
Aggressive drive, 70
  sublimations of, 79, 100
Agrippa, Cornelius, 11
Alexander, Franz, 16 n., 38 n.
Ambivalence, 86
American Psychiatric Association, 119
Anal character, 61 n.
Anal stage, 59
  character traits from, 60
Anderson, Victor V., 113
Animal magnetism, 15
Anthropology, 94
  psychiatry and, 34
  psychoanalysis and, 36
Anxiety, defenses against, 78, 85
Appel, John W., 2 n., 18 n.
Appel, Kenneth, 98 n.
Aristotle, 9
Army, discharges from, 2
  preventive psychiatry in, 18
  psychiatrists' role in, 126
Art, psychoanalysis and, 87
Aurelianus, Caelius, 9
Authority, attitude toward, 86

Beebe, Gilbert W., 18 n.
Benedict, Ruth, 35, 36 n., 37
Bennett, James V., 121 n.

Bernheim, H., 16
Bibring, Greta D., 31 n.
Blain, Daniel, 30 n.
Bowman, Harold Leonard, 43 n.
Braceland, Francis J., 19 n.
Braid, James, 16
Brenman, Margaret, 16 n., 29 n.
Bristol, Leverett D., 113 n.
Bronner, Augusta, 78 n.

Catholic University of America, 46
Character traits, from anal stage, 60
  from oral stage, 57
Charcot, Jean Martin, 16
Chisholm, G. Brock, 92 n., 106 n.
Clinical psychology, field of, 27
Commitment laws, to state hospitals, 116
Community, 103
Conscience, 75
Conscious, 67
Conversion, 84
Council for Clinical Training, 45
Counseling, in colleges, 109
  in industry, 114
  marriage, 30
  mental hygiene, 109

Court advisors, psychiatrists as, 119

Crimes, number of, 121

Criminal, psychiatric attitude toward, 120

public attitude toward, 122

Criminology, psychiatry and, 21, 115

Cyrus, Della D., 103 n.

Deutsch, Albert, 14 n.

Devereux, George, 35

Discharges from Army, 2

Displacement, 81

Divorce, extent of, 101

Dix, Dorothea Lynn, 14

Dollard, Charles, 39

Draft registrations, 2

Dreams, 66, 74

Dubois, Cora, 36 n.

Dunbar, Flander, 113 n.

Education, psychiatry and, 21, 106

Ego, 68, 73, 85

Ego defenses, 78

Elliotson, John, 15

Energy drives, 65

Environment, role in mental illness, 94

Erotic drive, 70

Esclepiades, 9

Evans, Lester J., 47

Expert testimony, 118

Fairbanks, Rollin J., 44 n.

Families with no children, 102

Family, 101

Federal Council of Churches of Christ in America, 46

Fenichel, Otto, 58 n., 61 n.

Ferenczi, Sandor, 65 n.

Flagellation, 10

Flaschner, Franklin N., 117 n.

Forgetting, 67

Frazer, J. G., 8 n.

Freud, Anna, 73 n., 78 n.

Freud, Sigmund, 6, 16, 17, 50, 51, 52, 53, 55 n., 64, 65, 68 n., 70, 79, 86 n., 87 n.

Galdston, Iago, 9 n., 15, 17, 88

Galen, 9

Genital stage, 62

Gill, Merton M., 16 n.

Ginsburg, Ethel L., 32 n.

Greek era, psychiatry in, 8

Gregg, Alan, 29 n., 46

Group for Advancement of Psychiatry, "statement on" religion, 24 n., 33 n., 42, 117 n.

Gruenberg, Sidonie M., 103 n.

Guttmacher, Manfred, 117 n.

Hall, J. K., 34 n.

Hamrin, Shirley Austin, 111 n.

Harrower, Molly, 28

Hartman, Heinz, 38 n.

Healy, William, 78 n.

Hendrick, Ives, 53 n., 63 n.

Hippocrates, 8

Housing, effect on mental health, 104
Hypnosis, 16, 66

Id, 68, 69
Idealization, mechanisms of, 81
Identification, role in mental health, 130
Individual, social order and, 95
  stresses on, 96
Industry, psychiatry and, 112
Infancy, mechanisms of, 78 n.
Infantile masturbation, 62
Instincts, 70
Institute of Pastoral Care, 44
Intolerance, 104
Isolationism, 103

Jails, 123
Jarrett, Mary C., 31
Jelliffe, Smith Ely, 9 n.
Jenkinson, Bruce L., 101 n.
Jones, Ernest, 61 n., 68 n., 79 n.
Jones, Howard M., 111

Kluckhohn, Clyde, 34 n., 37 n.
Koos, Earl L., 40 n., 105 n.

Labor-management disputes, 104
Leadership, effect on mental health, 127
Levine, Maurice, 19 n.
Levy, David, 110
Lewis, Nolan D. C., 9 n.
Liébeault, Ambrose-Auguste, 16
Liebman, Joshua Loth, 43 n.

Literature, psychoanalysis and, 87

Magician, 7
Malleus Maleficarum, 11
Marriage counseling, 30
Marshall, Helen E., 14 n.
Masturbation, infantile, 62
Maturity, psychological, 72, 99
Mead, Margaret, 35
Medical education, psychiatry and, 24
Medicine, psychiatry and, 22
Menninger, Jeanetta L., 70 n.
Menninger, Karl, 27 n., 28 n., 31 n., 63 n., 70 n., 71 n., 79 n., 108 n., 116 n., 119 n.
Mental health, effect of housing on, 104
  effect of leadership on, 127
  motivation and, 129
  role of identification in, 130
Mental Health Act, 25 n., 125
Mental health education, 99
Mental hygiene counseling, 109
Mental hygiene courses, 111
Mental illness, early treatment of, 14
  extent of, 98
Mental mechanisms, 77
Mesmer, Franz Anton, 15
Military service, discharges from, 97
Misbehavior, social, 123
Morris, Albert, 121 n.

Motivation, mental health and, 129

Neurotic behavior, 64
"Normal," definition of, 4

Oberndorf, Clarence P., 16
Oedipus situation, 63 n.
"Open-door" policy, 14
"Oral character," 58 n.
Oral stage, 57
  character traits from, 58

Paracelsus, 11, 15
Parsons, T. Alcott, 39 n.
Penitentiaries, federal, 122
Penology, psychiatry and, 122
Personality, courses on, 110
  definition of, 4
Personality disorders, 5
Physical symptoms, emotional origin of, 84
Pigott, George F., Jr., 111 n.
Pinel, Philippe, 13
Plato, 9
"Pleasure-pain principle," 55
Pound, Roscoe, 115
Prejudice, 104
Preventive psychiatry, 125
  in Army, 18
"Primitive" behavior, 35
Prisoners, number of, 121
Projection, 83
Psychiatric social work, 31
Psychiatry, dynamic, 17
  history of, 6

misconceptions of, 19
  "organic" approach to, 13
  preventive, in Army, 18
Psychoanalysis, anthropology and, 36
  art and, 87
  basic tenets of, 49
  literature and, 87
  meaning of, 51
  religion and, 41
  social group behavior and, 87
Psychoanalytic psychiatry, 49
Psychological tests, 27
Psychology, 94
  psychiatry and, 26
Psychoses, 76
Psychosexual development, 52
Psychosomatic medicine, 5
Public health, psychiatry in, 124
Public Health Service, 125

Rapaport, David, 27 n.
Rationalization, 80
Rawson, Arnold, 114 n.
Reading, remedial, 30
"Reality principle," 55
Reformatories, 123
Religion, goals of, 43
  psychiatry and, 41
  psychoanalysis and, 41, 87
Religious influence, historical, 10
Repression, 74, 78
Roheim, Gaza, 35
Ross, Elizabeth, 33 n.

Salmon, Thomas W., 17
Sapir, Edward, 35 n.
Shakow, David, 29 n.
Shepard, C. E., 111
Sickness proneness, 114
Social action, 100
Social adjustment, courses in, 110
Social case work, 31
Social group behavior, psycho-analysis and, 87
Social issues, psychiatrists' role in, 126
Social misbehavior, psychiatry and, 123
Social order, individual and, 95
  psychiatry and, 89
Social work, psychiatry and, 31
Sociology, 94
  psychiatry and, 38
Southard, Elmer E., 31, 112
Speech, slips of, 66
Speech training, 30
State hospitals, commitment laws to, 116
Stauffer, Samuel, 39
Stephen, Karin, 63 n.
Sublimation, 79
  in vocation, 80
Super-Ego, 63, 69, 74

Tarantula dances, 10
Teacher, in an American public school, 108
Teacher colleges, psychiatry in, 111
Testimony of experts, 118
Toilet training, 59
Tuke, William, 14

Unconscious, 63

Vocation, sublimation in, 80
Vocational adjustment, 30

War, cost of, 91
  forces that lead to, 106
  influence on psychiatry, 17
Wearn, Joseph T., 26 n.
Wechsler, Israel S., 79 n.
Weyer, Johan, 11
Whitman, Howard, 46 n.
Wife, role of, 102
Witchcraft, 11
Witch doctor, 7
Witmer, Helen, 35 n., 36 n.
Women working, number of, 101

Zilboorg, Gregory, 8 n., 11 n., 34 n.
Zinsser, Hans, 10 n.